The Frederick M. Watkins Collection

Fogg Art Museum

Harvard University

Library of Congress Catalog Card Number: 72-97-716

Printed in the United States of America

The catalogue was published on the occasion of the
exhibition, **The Frederick M. Watkins Collection**
January 31-March 14, 1973

Photographs by Michael Nedzweski, Fogg Art Museum.

Preface

The objects presented by Frederick M. Watkins to the Fogg Art Museum constitute the most important single group ever given to its Department of Ancient Art. Their quality is paramount. The calyx-krater by the Kleophrades Painter may unhesitatingly be described as the most superb Greek vase in the Museum's collection and one of the finest in America. The bronze Aphrodite is a miniature masterpiece; the ancient coins consistently reveal the collector's unwavering eye for beauty.

We are deeply indebted to Professor Watkins's sister, Miss Mary Watkins, for her eager assistance in all aspects of preparing the exhibition. Through her kindness we have been able to examine Professor Watkins's records and incorporate much important information into the catalogue text. Our sincere thanks go also to the authors, particularly our colleagues at other institutions, who have generously contributed catalogue entries on objects within their specialized fields. Dr. Leo Mildenberg and Mrs. Sylvia Herter provided valuable advice on the ancient coins, and Dr. Herbert A. Cahn offered useful information on many of the classical objects.

We warmly thank Michael Taylor, Keeper of the Coin Room at the Fogg, and Marion True and Claire Blackwell of the Museum of Fine Arts, Boston, for assisting with the preparation of the sections on coins and medals. Arthur Beale and David Rinne of the Fogg Conservation Department were indispensable in the conservation and technical examination of objects from the collection. We also thank Giovanna Vitelli, a student volunteer in that department, for her help in cleaning and mending several pieces. Diana Buitron offered important assistance in the initial planning stages and has graciously allowed us to adapt several entries from her earlier catalogue, *Attic Vase Painting in New England Collections* (1972). Finally, our hearty thanks go to Jill Brinnon and Barbara Kroll, who cheerfully coped with the complex details that will make a successful catalogue and exhibition, equal to the quality of the material that Frederick Watkins gave to Harvard.

Daniel Robbins
Director

We first met in 1935 as Junior Fellows at Harvard and became good personal friends, but it was quite some time thereafter that Fred Watkins mentioned his collection – in passing and diffidently. "You know I have some Greek coins"; the statement was so unemphatic that I took time to follow the lead. Eventually he showed me the coins, then in Providence, and I was astonished by the discriminating judgment to which their choice quality attested, a judgment that I had not expected from one so young.

Collecting had come to Fred early. He had been a frail, ailing child, yet one with a most active mind. His mother suggested coins as a hobby and introduced him to Henry Greene of Providence, a realtor, friend of the family, and collector of Greek coins, whose inspiration Fred always acknowledged with emphasis. Fred's sister, Miss Mary Watkins, recalls how the elderly collector would call Fred in great excitement whenever he had made a "catch," and how Fred soon reciprocated. As a student in Moses Brown School he had already formed a nucleus of Greek coins. As an undergraduate, he was placing bids at major international auctions through such leading numismatic firms as A. H. Baldwin of London, J. Hirsch of Geneva, and later O. Ravel of Marseilles. Fred's keen sense of beauty was manifesting itself. In 1928, after executing some bids for Fred, Dr. Jacob Hirsch wrote to the eighteen-year-old Harvard junior, then staying with his family at Berlin's famed Hotel Adlon, "I should very much like to make your personal acquaintance." Thus began an association which was of great importance for Fred's career as collector. Keen scholar of numismatics and the acknowledged *doyen* of all dealers in ancient art, Dr. Hirsch (1874-1955) was an unforgettable personality with a courtly manner and the appearance of a *grand seigneur*. He was one of that remarkable generation of scholar-dealers who had trained at universities, mostly in Germany and Italy, in the late nineteenth and early twentieth centuries, and who had brought dealing in ancient art to a high estate. Dr. Hirsch met the young collector with careful advice and with a sympathy not devoid of admiration for Fred's taste. As one of his associates recalls, whenever a particularly beautiful coin came to Dr. Hirsch, he would remark, "This is one for Watkins." Conversely, it was characteristic of Fred that he implicitly trusted Dr. Hirsch and considered him his foremost mentor in ancient art.

During Fred's college and graduate years there were other influences at work as well. Fred always mentioned gratefully Dean George Henry Chase's course in Greek archaeology, which he took at Harvard. Chase did much to confirm Fred in his belief that classical Greek art was the one art worthy of his special devotion. At the Fogg Museum, an afterglow of the glory of the pre-World War I era of collecting was kept alive by those incurable preachers of private collecting, Edward W. Forbes and Paul J. Sachs. The atmosphere created by their contagious enthusiasm was not without effect upon the young graduate.

It was in the late thirties and early forties that Fred stepped beyond numismatics and his taste in objects began to show its distinctive direction. Without fanfare, he built a splendid collection of Attic vases – ranging from the "Group E" black-figure amphora, through Onesimos, Makron, Douris, the Berlin Painter, the Providence Painter – an illustrious company. The artistic ideal thus circumscribed remained Fred's focal point to the end – the later archaic style of Greek art, especially in its more monumental aspects, and the lofty reserved dignity of early and high classical drawing, which struck a related chord in his being. Yet as the subjects of some of the vases attest, Fred's Hellas was not all dignified nobility; he had a lively appreciation of the whim and vigor of classical vitality.

In vases again, the quality was impressive. Sir John Beazley, who knew tens of thousands of Attic vases, wrote about Fred's Berlin Painter lekythos (December 26, 1941), "This is the sort of vase I should very much like to own if the price were within my means" – a supreme accolade from the masterly arbiter of all vase studies.

Fred was reserved and gentlemanly in his collecting negotiations; but once he had decided, he was swift, venturesome, and determined. His means were in no way comparable to those of the collecting giants of the 1920's, but he attained extraordinary results. The apogee of his collecting career was probably reached in 1941, when he emerged the victor in a triangular contest for a unique prize, the great Dionysiac krater depicting the return of Hephaistos, by the Kleophrades Painter. Field Marshal Hermann Goering, then at the height of his power, was determined to secure the piece. Dr. Hirsch, however, offered it first to the Metropolitan Museum, and when the museum did not act, gave Fred preference over all other buyers.

In the earlier part of his career, Fred had occasionally considered objects other than vases – the Attic doll, for instance, was bought from a private owner because Chase had brought it to Fred's attention. However, it was not until after World War II and after Dr. Hirsch's death that he widened his interest to include bronzes and other sculptures. He put much trust in the judgment of Charles L. Morley but would occasionally survey the field in New York and on his rare trips to Europe. He would quite suddenly either phone or appear at my door, explaining in a few quick words his present project and at times proposing a joint visit to a gallery. It was always a fascinating experience. Unlike some famous collectors whose enthusiasm is all-encompassing and who narrow down their choices by comparison and elimination, Fred seemed nearly always to know what he was looking for and was willing to wait for it. Nor was he, though a scholar and scientist by training and profession, a "scholarly collector" of the kind who can take fire over a piece that is interesting and unusual for historical, social, economic, or religious reasons. He would make a point of securing highly competent advice – only too often did I discover that my attempts to instruct Fred were way behind the information he had already assembled. Although he never verbalized on this point, it was clear that the aesthetic essence of a work of art was what spoke to him – and he waited for the work that would speak.

The severe discipline imposed by his solitary quest was combined with extraordinary sensitivity and sureness of eye. His collection was remarkably free of second-rate or merely "interesting" pieces. He was the only collector I have known whose choices were faulted rather than aided by advice and advisors. Essentially, his own decisions were the ones that were right. A collector, like a saint, requires good deeds; like a saint, no collector is exempt from sin. Thus, early in his career he bought two rhyta which were then universally believed to be ancient art, but were later unmasked as modern by J. D. Beazley. Among his subsequent acquisitions, there is one which was strongly approved by his advisors, but has since been questioned as possibly a clever modern cast after an ancient piece.

Yet when all is said and done, the portrait of Fred Watkins as a collector emerges most clearly from such masterly objects as the krater by the Kleophrades Painter, the marble head in a near-Phidian style, the bronzes of the splendid Arcadian "poet" and of the solemn Aphrodite, and one of his last purchases, a much-cherished one, the eloquent kalpis showing the ransom of Hector's noble corpse.

Almost by definition, collectors are expansive and want the world to acclaim audibly and publicly their cherished possessions. Such jubilation was not for Fred, but if he heard scholars and students whose judgment he valued praise and rejoice in one of his objects, a brief moment of warm glow would permeate his very being, showing how strongly he loved and how much he appreciated the sharing of his own deeply felt experience of classical art.

Collecting was for Fred Watkins a real need, one which his taste and mind craved to satisfy, yet he did not collect for himself. In speaking of his aims and objectives as collector he was undemonstrative and sparing of words, but I have reason to believe that he thought about the destiny of his collection with utmost care. He was a man of deep-rooted loyalties and broad vision, and if his collection has now come to the Fogg Art Museum, we may be sure that both gratitude for early stimulation in his undergraduate days and trust in the future determined his choice.

George M. A. Hanfmann
John E. Hudson Professor of Archaeology, Harvard University
Curator of Ancient Art, Fogg Art Museum

Frederick M. Watkins, the Political Scientist

Fred Watkins was one of the outstanding scholars in the field of political theory and its history. Beginning with his undergraduate distinction thesis *(summa cum laude)* dealing with Charles Maurras and with the political theory of the *Action Française*, he steadily contributed books and articles to this difficult field. His work always had a distinction of its own, through its admirable style and the clarity of its thought. He had little patience with fads. He did not suffer fools gladly. His sharp criticism of Pareto's verbalism was as cutting as his rejection of recent methodological trends in political science.

He was a traditionalist in the best sense. His eminence in his chosen field found suitable expression in his being elected president of the American Society of Political and Legal Philosophy. He did not aspire to such positions and honors. They came to him almost against his wish, foisted upon him as a recognition of his unusual intellectual capacities by admiring colleagues. During the war, he participated at Harvard in the China and Japan programs of the School for Overseas Administration, and with characteristic thoroughness he plunged into the study of these languages, mastering Chinese sufficiently to teach his officer students on the basis of the original texts.

Fred Watkins was, as his collection shows, a man of exceptionally good taste; fortunately by inheritance he was enabled to engage his passion for beauty in music as well as in the arts. He had a winsome, yet slightly mocking mode of speaking and writing, mistaken by some sentimentalists for sarcasm. His most important work, *The Political Tradition of the West* (1948), manifests Watkins's marked esthetic sense of form and balance. The political tradition of the West seemed to him essentially a humanist liberalism, skeptical of man and his use of power. It was a tradition to which Watkins was firmly attached. It was also a tradition he saw waning.

This essay of historical philosophizing had been preceded by a small but very weighty study, *The State as a Concept of Political Science* (1934). Watkins wrote it as one of the members of the Society of Fellows at Harvard, being one of the very first group of Fellows elected to this prestigious body of young scholars. This book is deeply traditional in considering the state as "a sovereign association," and sovereignty as "omnipotence within a territorially delimited segment of human society." I did not and do not agree, but I consider it the best statement of this widely prevalent theory. The essay ought to be reprinted, having long been unavailable.

Another fruit of the years of unhampered creativity for Fred Watkins at the Society of Fellows was his incisive study of the road to Hitler, *The Failure of Constitutional Emergency Powers under the German Republic* (1939). His conclusion that "inadequate emergency arrangements prevent the force of constitutional government from being brought to an effective focus" has not lost any of its cogency in our day. That "the supporters of the Weimar Republic might have prevailed in an actual show of force" would not now be conceded by most historians and political scientists. Watkins's strong doubt that the lesson had been learned embittered his last years and filled him with poignant pessimism over the future of humanist liberalism and the political tradition of America. Who can say that he was wrong? Who would not sympathize with his flight into the realm of beauty which has so often been the refuge of the man of spirit in the days of violence?

Carl J. Friedrich
Eaton Professor of the Science of Government, Emeritus Harvard University

Frederick M. Watkins: The Harvard Days

No one who knew Fred Watkins well would dare write the usual memoir. Aristotle's third branch of rhetoric, the laudatory and ceremonial, was very far from Fred's own jesting, ironical, and somehow very humane style. Once late at night, we walked from Boston to Cambridge after an evening of theater, as was often his practice. His furious walking speed, for me almost a half trot, did not keep him from reading the inscription at the base of a statue of a Boston worthy. "Someday," he said thoughtfully, "I hope to find a dedication that reads, 'Hancock Revere, soldier, patriot, statesman – and son-of-a-bitch'."

Fred's friends learned to know him during those long midnight walks, for which he was always ready – often up one side of the Charles to Watertown and back down again, covering Harvard faculty politics, the sociological theories of Wilhelm Dilthey, Mayor Curley's combination of highly practical politics and eloquence. Nothing human was strange to Fred, or without its supply of amusement. He recorded with pleasure the fact that he had misquoted a positive for a negative in his own doctoral thesis and no one had ever noticed; he discussed with equal pleasure his problems with his German lute-maker and his discovery that one could then buy obscene Greek vases rather cheaply because museums found it difficult to exhibit them.

For a time we were also able to go single sculling up the Charles with Fred, until bursitis of the arms made this most pleasant of all Harvard sports impossible for him. One memorable day Fred and I took out a double scull. We could not coordinate our strokes, our backslides, or our progress. Finally a police launch, which had watched with amazement our skate-bug zigzags, across, up and down the Charles River, escorted us firmly back to our launch pad. We concluded, Fred and I, that Harvard had indeed made true individuals out of us.

As undergraduates in the thirties we were far too poor to go to the theater, which Fred, then a tutor at Lowell House, dearly loved, as much as he loved company. And so he developed an intricate system of theatrical loans to several of us, which in my case were not paid off for some years, and which, I am sure, in his delicate way he unobtrusively lowered and misremembered from performance to performance. There was one complication about going to the theater with Fred – if the play was poor, or poorly performed, you had to walk out in the middle. He liked to quote (against himself) the challenge of the usher as we walked out in the middle of a very bad Saroyan play. "Too deep for you?" asked the usher. "Yes," said Fred, delighted with this question, which from then on became part of his rich repertory of ironical phrases.

Fred saw not only every play but almost every movie that came to Boston and Cambridge, claiming in his lighthearted way that it was his one touch with the common man. Those were the days of packed movie houses, but Fred always found room in the first row, where he sat armed with an evening's supply of wintergreen lifesavers – there was always room there. Fred was not only a political but a social theorist, with many half seriously held views of human behavior. It was one of his theories that long association, as in a marriage, made people look like each other. An extension of this theory was his notion that you somehow came to resemble your profession. He always nudged me in our favorite Cambridge movie palace when a Harvard anthropologist who also liked the front rows slouched, almost chimpanzee-like, into his seat.

Long before it was the fashion, Fred had strong, clear views on gourmet dining. His model was a well-known collector of first editions whose habit it was, when an entrée displeased him, to dump the offending platter upside down on the floor. For Fred the two great cuisines were French and Chinese. When I knew him he had pretty well given up all hope of finding a perfectly cooked French dish, such as an artichoke, and was concentrating on Boston's Chinatown. To meet his standards a great Chinese restaurant had to be able to serve, to perfection, at least egg foo yong, butterfly shrimp, Cantonese lobster, and what he called "one peasant dish." From a wealthy Kuomintang student of his who always carried two tennis rackets (even into his political science tutorials with Fred), he had learned that the greatest banquets included, for contrast, one peasant dish. The notion struck Fred's delicate sense of irony and became law.

On his own family farm, where his sister Mary did much of the work, he specialized in one American dish, hot fresh buttered corn. This had to be cut from the steaming cobs, and how our fingers burned as we sliced away under his demanding eye, wasting not a single precious kernel from the ears, which had to be picked at dawn. He could eat whole bowlfuls at a time.

At his farm or his home we could have a better idea of his taste and range as a collector of vases and coins from classical Greece. But I also recall the joy with which he told how his maid picked up a coin showing Leda and the swan and asked in some horror, "What's that duck doing?"

It was Fred's pleasure each year to give a lobster thermidor party at the well-known Boston restaurant, Locke-Ober. Lobster thermidor – according to Fred – because nothing else cost more, or made the chef work harder, or was more complicated. One evening I hired an excruciatingly bad accordionist to play for half an hour in front of Locke-Ober. It was the kind of joke of which the highly musical Fred was fondest. A somewhat stuffy newcomer to our group, a fellow tutor of Fred's (the rest of us were all students), took Fred aside and said, of me, that he hated to see someone who could not hold his liquor. When we returned to Fred's quarters for a nightcap, he made sure that his colleague received a highball glass full of bourbon, then gleefully helped us all carry him off to bed as we sang in the Lowell House courtyard, "Oh violate me in the vilest way in violet time."

A few weeks later it was my turn, having talked too much about Sigmund Freud. By the verdict of our group, Fred hired a taxi, and as all the others sat on my head, conveyed me out to Walden Pond and threw me in. Everyone then joined this midnight swim, including the taxi driver, if I remember correctly, and we returned, suitably cleansed.

A major part of Fred's life was music. We often played together – two-piano duets in which I played his harpsichord and he played the piano, or Mozart and Haydn symphonies which he dearly loved in the fourhand piano arrangements. Or we would have fipple flute concerts, to the continuo of his harpsichord – with Fred himself playing his pride, the bass fipple flute, which he could make sound something like a tuba. Part of his repertory of ironic sayings was the remark of his music teacher, who had once commended his piano with exquisite patronage by observing, "You are very good, for an amateur."

Fred tried the violin but admitted freely that he played it badly. It was his habit to go to a practice room high in the Lowell House tower and there open all the windows in springtime and play into the evening darkness. One evening when he was in unusual form and no one below could figure out the source of these unearthly wailings, a rioting crowd of several hundred Harvard students formed and eventually, as was then the practice, marched over to Radcliffe for still more rioting there. Fred came down from the tower after they had left, inquiring where everyone had gone. Perhaps he learned of his triumph later. Shortly after this incident, he abandoned his violin.

In the late thirties Fred gave up his stance as political theorist in the pure sense and became increasingly concerned about the rise of Hitler. He felt that his beloved French, like the Chinese, were among the most self-centered people on earth – one of his theories being that this characteristic enabled them to perfect their cuisines while their governments lost vitality. After France fell, unable to enter the services himself because of age and asthma, he tried to make himself useful by learning Chinese. This he successfully managed, arguing that anyone could learn to read Chinese by simply not bothering to associate Chinese sounds with the ideographic characters in which it was written. He liked to discuss (ironically) the differences between the version of the Chinese autobiography that Chiang Kai-shek had prepared for home consumption and that which he sent overseas. Most of all, Fred liked to imagine the last days of Hitler, when he would offer to accept unconditional surrender terms. General Fred then proposed to reply, "Unconditional surrender is not enough."

There are many ways of remembering Fred Watkins. He was, so I understand, a popular College Master in Canada and leader of a successful departmental revolt against his university president. It was his fantasy that, though he never learned to drive, he would some day acquire a pilot's license so as to become possibly the only airplane pilot who did not know how to drive an automobile. He was especially gifted at the delicate putdown. After we had listened to a student recount his amorous triumphs of that month, Fred said, kindly, "The prize stallions are not sent out to stud until they have won a few races."

But for me, I think of Fred Watkins asking, after an evening of theater or movies or music, "what shall it be, two bridges, three bridges, or the four miles to Watertown?" And once again we are off into the night, at his rapid pace, with the whole world the object of his delicate, ironically inquiring mind.

John Ashmead

Contributors to the Catalogue

Ann H. Ashmead	AHA
Jill W. Brinnon	JWB
Diana Buitron	DB
Suzannah Doeringer	SD
George M. A. Hanfmann	GMAH
Louisa M. F. Huber	LMFH
David G. Mitten	DGM
Kyle M. Phillips	KMP
Jane C. Waldbaum	JCW

R. Ross Holloway

Mary Comstock
Cornelius Vermeule

Compiler's Note

All dimensions are given in inches and meters and are assumed to represent the maximum dimension unless otherwise stated. L. and r. indicate the object's, or proper, left and right. Bibliographical abbreviations follow the *American Journal of Archaeology,* 74 (1970), 3-8, or the list opposite.

Bibliographic Abbreviations

Art and Technology
S. Doeringer, D. G. Mitten, and A. Steinberg, eds., *Art and Technology* (Cambridge, Mass., 1970).

ARV
J. D. Beazley, *Attic Red-Figure Vase Painters* (Oxford, 1963).

BMFA, *Bronzes*
M. Comstock and C. C. Vermeule, *Greek, Etruscan and Roman Bronzes* (Greenwich, Conn., 1971).

Buitron, *Attic Vases*
D. M. Buitron, *Attic Vase Painting in New England Collections* (Exhibition catalogue, Fogg Art Museum, Cambridge, Mass., 1972).

Charbonneaux, *Bronzes*
J. Charbonneaux, *Les bronzes grecs* (Paris, 1958).

CVA
Corpus Vasorum Antiquorum

FAM Acquisitions
Fogg Art Museum Acquisitions (Cambridge, Mass., 1959–).

Fogg, *Ancient Art*
Ancient Art in American Private Collections (Exhibition catalogue, Fogg Art Museum, Cambridge, Mass., 1954).

Fogg, *Master Bronzes*
D. G. Mitten and S. Doeringer, *Master Bronzes from the Classical World* (Exhibition catalogue, Fogg Art Museum, Cambridge, Mass., 1968).

Giglioli, *AE*
G. Q. Giglioli, *L'arte etrusca* (Milan, 1935).

Jantzen, *Bronzewerkstätten*
U. Jantzen, *Bronzewerkestätten in Grossgriechenland und Sizilien, Jdl,* Ergänzungsheft xiii (Berlin, 1937).

Lamb, *Bronzes*
W. Lamb, *Greek and Roman Bronzes* (London, 1929).

Langlotz, *S. Italy*
E. Langlotz, *Ancient Greek Sculpture of South Italy and Sicily* (New York, 1965).

Neugebauer, *Katalog*
K. A. Neugebauer, *Katalog der statuarischen Bronzen im Antiquarium,* Staatliche Museen zu Berlin, Vol II, *Die griechischen Bronzes der Klassischen Zeit und des Hellenismus* (Berlin, 1951).

Noble,*Techniques*
J. V. Noble, *The Technique of Painted Attic Pottery* (New York, 1965).

Paralipomena
J. D. Beazley, *Paralipomena: Additions to Attic Black-Figure Vase-Painters and to Attic Red-Figure Vase-Painters* (2nd ed.; Oxford, 1971.)

Richter, *Bronzes*
G.M.A. Richter, *Greek, Etruscan and Roman Bronzes* (New York, 1915).

Richter, *Furniture*
G.M.A. Richter, *The Furniture of the Greeks, Etruscans and Romans* (London, 1966).

Schefold, *Meisterwerke*
K. Schefold, *Meisterwerke griechischer Kunst,* Kunsthalle Basel, June 18-September 13, 1960 (Basel, 1960).

Teitz, *Etruscan*
R. S. Teitz, *Masterpieces of Etruscan Art* (Exhibition catalogue, Worcester Art Museum, Worcester, Mass., 1967).

1

Griffin Protome

Greek, ca. 625-600 B.C.

Bronze, H. 7¼ in. (0.184 m.); Diam. at base 2¾ in. (0.071 m.)

Hollow cast. Dark green patina. Intact, except for missing tips of ears. Incised decoration.

Provenance: Said to have been found at Olympia. S. Morgenroth to Charles L. Morley; to Frederick M. Watkins; Gift to the Fogg Art Museum, Harvard University, 1963.130.

This griffin protome is one of a pair, the other of which cannot at present be located. Rivets in the flange around the base of the neck fastened it and its companions to the shoulder of a large hammered bronze cauldron. The curving, swelling forms of the mythical monster are enriched with painstakingly incised ornament, including tiny scales on the neck (probably produced with a lunate punch); a wide S-shaped lock on either side of the neck, terminating in a curl; and minute incisions along the edges of the upright ears, perhaps representing fine fur. The hollow eyes were probably once inlaid.

   Griffins, composite creatures probably of Near Eastern origin, are prominent participants in the animal parades on Greek pottery of the late seventh century B.C.; they battle Arimaspians while protecting golden treasure in the far northern regions. Cast griffin protomes, perhaps performing a guardian function for the cauldrons to which they were attached, have been found in numbers at Olympia and especially at the Heraion on Samos. Miscast specimens recovered at the latter sanctuary strongly suggest that they were manufactured on Samos (U. Jantzen, *Griechische Greifenkessel* [Berlin, 1955], pls. 17-18). The choice between a Samian or Peloponnesian workshop for the Watkins protome is difficult; its date, the last quarter of the seventh century B.C., can be fixed with much greater confidence. The Watkins griffin belongs to Jantzen's "Fourth Group" of cast protomes, in which the neck locks are still depicted. His date, in the second half of the seventh century (pp. 69-70; 84-85), seems too early. For a set of three comparable protomes, with a fragment of the rim of their cauldron, cf. BMFA, *Bronzes,* 283, no. 407.

DGM

Bibliography: Fogg, *Ancient Art,* 30, no. 199, pl. 60; J. L. Benson, "Unpublished Griffin Protomes in American Collections," *AntK,* 3 (1960), 58-70, appendix; M. Del Chiaro, *Greek Art from Private Collections of Southern California* (exhibition catalogue, University of California at Santa Barbara, 1963), 8, no. 2, ill.; D. G. Mitten, "Two Griffin Protomes," *FAM Acquisitions,* 1964, 11-19, ill.; Fogg, *Master Bronzes,* 73, no. 67, ill.

2

Base Plate of a Hydria Handle: Kore and Gorgon

Greek, Laconian, ca. 560-550 B.C.

Bronze, H. 4⁷⁄₁₆ in. (0.114 m.); W. 3¼ in. (0.082 m.)

Solid cast plate; stump of hollow handle appears to be filled with a ferrous substance. Mottled dark green patina. A few tiny pits from gas bubbles created during casting visible on l. ear and eye of gorgon. Smooth edge on r., contrasting to protruding spiral on l., suggests that the piece may not have filled out completely in casting. Surface shows effects of drastic mechanical cleaning in modern times.

Provenance: Said to come from Greece. B. Zoumboulakis, Geneva, to Frederick M. Watkins; Gift to the Fogg Art Museum, Harvard University, 1962.178.

This fragment served to attach the lower end of a vertical handle to the shoulder of an unusually large, elaborate hydria. The spiral at the left side of the gorgon's head is positioned similarly to the tails of the reclining rams flanking gorgons' heads on less elaborate handles; these tails lend additional strength at a critical spot and camouflage the rivets that attached handle to vase (cf. handles in Boston, inv. nos. 01.7474 and 99.462; ram, inv. no. 52.188; BMFA, *Bronzes,* 288-289, nos. 413-414, and 292, no. 417).

Single gorgon masks and heads of *korai* (maidens) are frequent ornaments for the base plates of hydria handles. Von Bothmer associated the Watkins gorgon with Diehl's "Gorgoneion Group," to which the two handles in Boston belong (E. Diehl, *Die Hydria* [Mainz, 1964], 214-215). The horned Gorgon, however, is a special variety, discussed and identified as Lakonian by T. Karagiorga ("Lakonika Gorgoneia," *Deltion,* 19 [1964], A¹, 116-122). A less plausible view is that the horns are borrowed from the river god Acheloos (W. Hermann, "Gorgo und Acheloos," *RM,* 70 [1963], 1-3). By far the closest relatives to the Watkins gorgon are the horned gorgon on the base plate of a hydria handle from Trebenischte, in Sofia (B. Filow, *Die archaische Nekropole von Trebenischte* [Berlin, 1927], 54-55, no. 70, pl. 9), and the gorgons on the handle, rotelles, and frieze of the ornate bucchero oinochoe from Chiusi in Palermo (Museo Nazionale, inv. no. 6651).

The head of the *kore* is rendered with unusual care. Her hair is elaborately incised and plaited into three locks on each side; a hairband holds back the scalloped locks framing her forehead. At her throat is a necklace or the beaded edge of a garment. Her gaunt, wide-eyed expression and downturned, asymmetrical mouth, together with her large ears and still faintly Daedalic-looking wig, are reminiscent of monumental sculpture from early in the sixth century B.C. (Compare especially the heads of Kleobis and Biton from Delphi, G.M.A. Richter, *Kouroi,* 2nd ed. [London, 1960], 49-50, nos. 12 A and B, figs. 78-83, 91, 92.) Among single kore protomes, one on the handle of the "Telestas Hydria" in Mainz is the closest to the Watkins bronze (G. Hafner, "Die Hydria des Telestas," *Charites* [Bonn, 1957], 119-126).

In its juxtaposition of kore and gorgon, the Watkins handle fragment appears to be unique. It is unclear why the two, "Beauty and the Beast," should be shown together. Although it has been suggested that the bronze represents Athena furnished with an enormous *gorgoneion* as aegis, this interpretation seems unlikely.

Because of the strong correspondences with early sixth-century sculpture, a date of ca. 570 B.C. was initially proposed. H. Jucker, however, places it later, but still before mid-century. A date of ca. 560-550 B.C. seems likely.

DGM

Bibliography: D. G. Mitten, "A Gorgon at the Fogg," *FAM Acquisitions,* 1962-63, 11-16; D. von Bothmer, *Gnomon,* 37 (1965), 600; H. Jucker, *Bronzehenkel und Bronzehydria in Pesaro* (Pesaro, 1966), 47, 111-112, no. 367, pl. 37; Fogg, *Master Bronzes,* 76, no. 71, ill.

3

Winged Mirror Caryatid

Greek, South Italian, Tarentine (?), ca. 550-525 B.C.

Bronze, H. 7⅞ in. (0.20 m.); W. 3¹⁵⁄₁₆ in. (0.10 m.)

Solid cast. Shiny green patina. Large cavity on rear, above r. ankle, is probably a casting defect. Ancient patch on underside of upper r. arm.

Provenance: Said to come from Greece. On art market, 1937; Jacob Hirsch to Frederick M. Watkins, 1941; Bequest to the Fogg Art Museum, Harvard University, 1972.56.

This slim maiden once served as the handle for a standing mirror. The mirror disk, which was cast separately, would have been attached to the support that rests atop the caryatid's head and wing tips. The repeating curves of her wings and arms form a graceful figure-eight, an effective transition between the strongly geometric forms of the spherical disk and columnar figure.

After the figure was cast, the artist lavished much attention on its decoration. Incised lines articulate the feathers, separate the long corrugated strands of hair in back, form a collar at the neck, and define the inner garment where it protrudes at the ankles beneath the outer one. Punched circles run along the hems of both garments; others at the shoulder seams indicate buttons. Punched semicircles adorn the inner margins of the wings, echoing the scalloped scale motif of the bodice, which perhaps represents feathers or armor.

Two unusual features mark the statuette: the arms akimbo and the use of wings to support the mirror. Jantzen (pp. 7-8) interprets the arm motif as emphasizing the heaviness of the caryatid's burden. He sees this device as occurring rarely, only during the first half of the sixth century, being later replaced by the motif of upstretched arms supporting the load. The gorgons from Trebenischte and a female figure in Berlin (Jantzen, pl. 26)—all from tripod supports—also have their hands on their hips.

Wings bearing the disk are virtually unknown among mirror caryatids. Although winged figures occur frequently on hand mirrors, the wings touch the disk without seeming to bear its weight (cf. Jantzen, pls. 6-7). Wings play a number of other "supporting roles" in bronzes of this period, however. Jantzen and Neugebauer discuss winged figures decorating the feet of vessels and tripod supports (Jantzen, Appendix 3B; K. A. Neugebauer,

"Reifarchaische Bronzevasen mit Zungenmuster," *RM,* 38-39 [1923-24], 425ff). The elaborate handle of the Grächwyl hydria (Schefold, *Meisterwerke,* 114, no. 107), though earlier than the bronzes in question, shows a goddess on whose wing tips the rim of the vase appears to rest. A similar relationship to the rim is found in a goddess in relief on a fragment from the neck of a Cretan clay pithos in Copenhagen (inv. no. 3375; *Art and Technology,* 151, fig. 7).

Many of these related pieces are associated with Tarentum; in addition, the facial features of the Watkins mirror caryatid bear similarities to Tarentine work of the period. These factors suggest that the bronze might be assigned to a Tarentine workshop. Jucker (p. 200) attributes it to Magna Graecia. K. A. Neugebauer, however, is quoted on Hirsch's bill of sale to Watkins as considering the bronze the earliest known caryatid of Corinthian workmanship.

The identity of the maiden remains open to question. Jantzen has called her a Nike (Victory), while Mitten, on the analogy of the Grächwyl handle, postulates that she represents the winged Artemis, the *potnia theron* (Mistress of Animals).

SD

Bibliography: Jantzen, *Bronzewerkstätten,* 7, no. 110, pl. 26; Fogg, *Master Bronzes,* 81, no. 75, ill.; H. Jucker, "Etruscan Votive Bronzes of Populonia," in *Art and Technology,* 200-203, cf. figs. 10, 11, discussing the arms-akimbo pose.

4

Bearded Man with a Staff

Greek, Arcadian, ca. 525-500 B.C.

Bronze, H. 4⅘ in. (0.122 m.)

Solid cast. Shiny dark green patina. Staff made separately and inserted through perforated r. hand and plinth.

Provenance: Acquired by Rhousopoulos at Argos, 1870; Jacob Hirsch to Frederick M. Watkins; Gift to the Fogg Art Museum, Harvard University, 1965.533.

This short but sturdy bearded man stands with both feet firmly planted upon a rectangular bronze plinth. He gazes slightly upward and to his left. His left arm is held firmly against his side beneath his drapery, while his right extends forward to grasp a staff that might identify him as a shepherd, poet, or herald. The slender, columnar shape of his body, dominated by strong, muscular shoulders and chest, is wrapped tightly in a cloak fastened over the left shoulder, leaving the right side bare to just beneath the breast. It clearly indicates the sinuous bulges of his torso, calves, and buttocks. The head, rather massive in proportion to the body, is richly incised with a wealth of detail. His hair, parted over the forehead and indicated by lines radiating from just beneath the crown, hangs to his shoulders and is held firmly by a dotted garland. Two slender braids, falling to the middle of his breast, are marked by tiny regular striations, as are his sideburns, beard, and moustache. An alert twinkling eye, snub nose, and broad, smiling mouth, combined with his powerfully muscular anatomy, convey a distinctive sense of physical and mental vitality.

The garment, similar to those worn by archaic bronze figures of Zeus, might suggest a god (D. G. Mitten) or a heroized Arcadian ruler (K. Schefold). However, the absence of any specific identifying characteristics makes it improbable that the figure represents a god. He might instead be compared with a rustic Arcadian shepherd in New York (Richter, p. 5), which is slightly less refined. There is also a striking similarity between the bronze and those figures of trainers in athletic scenes on early Attic red-figure pottery, such as the cup by Onesimos in the Watkins Collection (No. 22). The relationship to the "Warren" herm (BMFA, *Bronzes,* 27, no. 24, ill.) and to the shepherd in the Museum of Art, Rhode Island School of Design (inv. no. 20.056; Fogg, *Master Bronzes,* 61, no. 47, ill.) cannot be ignored.

JWB

Bibliography: Albright Art Gallery, *Master Bronzes Selected from Museums and Collections in America* (exhibition catalogue, Buffalo, 1937), no. 74, ill.; Fogg, *Ancient Art,* 31, no. 211, pl. 65; D. G. Mitten, "An Arcadian in the Fogg Museum," *Fogg Art Museum Newsletter,* 3:3 (February 1966), ill.; Fogg, *Master Bronzes,* 61, no. 48, ill. For comparative pieces, see Lamb, pls. 26c, 28c; G. M. A. Richter, "Five Bronzes Recently Acquired by the Metropolitan," *AJA,* 48 (1944), 5, figs. 11-13.

5

Seated Man

Greek, Attic, ca. 500 B.C.

Bronze, H. 2⅞ in. (0.074 m.); W. 2 in. (0.051 m.)

Solid cast. Dark green to brown patina. Surface corroded in places. R. leg missing below knee; l. leg missing below calf; both fractures appear to have occurred because of imperfections in the casting. Modern bolt inserted into underside of buttocks for attachment to wooden stand.

Provenance: Acquired by Captain E. G. Spencer-Churchill, 1915; Sale, London, Christie's, June 21, 1965, to Münzen und Medaillen A.G.; to Frederick M. Watkins, 1966; Bequest to the Fogg Art Museum, Harvard University, 1972.57.

Although tiny, this dynamically posed and robustly modeled figure has the commanding presence of a monumental sculpture. This effect is due in part to the head actively turned to the left, while the arms move in the opposite direction. The right hand appears to have grasped an upright shaft-like object, such as a spear or staff, while the clenched left fist, held lower and closer to the body, vividly conveys the tension of compressed strength.

The powerful chest and shoulders merge into a torso of pronounced planar modeling; as seen from the front, the sides of the torso are conspicuously concave. The outsides of the thighs, likewise planar, meet the curving inner surfaces in a sharp ridge. The musculature of arms and calves is delicately, clearly delineated. A sharp groove separates the lower abdomen from the upper thighs. The muscular divisions of the upper abdomen, bounded by the diaphragm, are bilaterally symmetrical. A crescentic crease arches above the navel; the genitalia are delicately rendered. The eyes, large rounded ovals, dominate the squarish face set on a thick neck. The hair is rendered as a thick cap with a scalloped, uprolled front edge; here, as in the beard, some of the fine incisions for individual strands of hair are still preserved. The upper edge of the beard is sharply separated from the cheeks.

In general, the anatomical and stylistic peculiarities of the statuette permit its dating to the end of the sixth or beginning of the fifth century B.C. The powerful head, with its broad, rounded forms, can be compared to late archaic marble heads from the Acropolis, the Agora, and the Athenian Treasury at Delphi, as well as with the head of the bronze statuette of Zeus from Dodona, in Berlin (H. Payne and G. Mackworth-Young, *Archaic Marble Sculptures from the Acropolis*, 2nd ed. [London, 1950], pls. 103-104; hair treatment especially close to that of the "Kritios Boy," pls. 111-112. For heads from the Athenian Treasury at Delphi, see P. de la Coste-Messelière, *Delphes* [Paris, 1943], pls. 126-127, 133, 134, 137. W. Schiering, *Die Bronzestatuette der Zeus von Dodona* [Stuttgart, 1969], fig. 1.).

The modeling of the abdominal structure is close to the "clinical" renderings of musculature on Attic red-figure vases by Euphronios and his contemporaries. It also resembles the torso of Herakles in the metope from the Athenian Treasury showing his combat with the stag. The squarish form of torso and buttocks is similar to that of certain Attic bronze statuettes of nude athletes found in the debris from the Persian sack of the Athenian Acropolis in 480 B.C. (cf. H.-G. Niemeyer, "Attische Bronzestatuetten der spätarchaischen und frühklassischen Zeit," *Antike Plastik*, 3:1 [Berlin, 1964], 7-31).

The statuette's attribution to an Athenian workshop becomes virtually certain when one compares it with a seated figure of identical size in the National Museum, Athens (inv. no. 6602; A. de Ridder, *Catalogue des bronzes trouvés sur l'Acropole d'Athènes* [Paris, 1896], 278, no. 754; 279, fig. 262; I am grateful to Mrs. Evi Touloupa, Curator of Bronzes, National Museum, for providing recent photographs of this statuette). Both statuettes are seated, yet dynamic. Their legs are together, and they share the same marked squareness of torso and buttocks. On both figures, too, the underside of the buttocks is a concave surface, designed to fit something—perhaps the rim or shoulder of a krater or other large vessel. One might suggest that the Watkins statuette and Athens 6602 are mates, originally decorating the same complex bronze vessel.

The identity of the figure is obscure. While a mortal or hero are possibilities, the heroic nudity and assertive, regal bearing suggest a major god—Zeus or Poseidon. The figure's upraised right hand could have supported a scepter or trident; the left hand might have clutched a thunderbolt or other smaller attribute.

DGM

Bibliography: Christie's, *Northwick Park Collection, Antiquities* [London, June 21, 1965], lot 110, no. 448, pl. 51; Fogg, *Master Bronzes*, 84, no. 78, ill.

6

Aphrodite with a Dove

Greek, ca. 450 B.C.

Bronze, H. 4³⁄₁₆ in. (0.107 m.)

Solid cast. Deep green patina with large reddish areas.
R. arm with bird cast separately; seam visible just below
r. shoulder. Bronze analyzed spectroscopically as
containing 8% tin. Iron pin in head; square ancient patch
in r. shoulder. Beak of bird broken off. Unusual thinning
of r. arm probably resulting from excessive mechanical
cleaning in modern times.

Provenance: Said to come from Epidauros. Frederick M.
Watkins; Gift to the Fogg Art Museum, Harvard
University, 1960.666.

Swathed only in a *himation* that encircles her in emphatic spiral folds, this small statuette conveys a sense of monumentality suggesting that it may reproduce some lost life-sized cult statue. Epidauros is known to have been a center for the worship of Aphrodite in the fourth century; if this statuette indeed comes from there, it may even echo the cult image of an earlier temple to the goddess at this site.

The solemnity, the treatment of eyes and mouth, and the elaborate, carefully rendered hairdo relate the bronze statuette closely to a series of Roman copies after a lost Greek original of the decade 470-460 B.C. (Hanfmann, *AJA*, 283). This so-called "Budapest type" has been seen by Langlotz and Schuchhardt to reflect a masterpiece by a major sculptor of the early classical style. Hanfmann correctly connects the Aphrodite to the group of works attributed to this unknown master, discussing stylistic analogies between it and such well-known bronzes as the Elgin Athena and the "Spinning Girl" in Berlin.

Several small bronzes depict a maiden with a dove in a pose not unlike the Watkins Aphrodite. Most notable are one in Berlin (inv. no. 8599; Neugebauer, *Katalog*, no. 21, pl. 16), and one in the Petit Palais (W. Froehner, *Collection Auguste Dutuit, bronzes antiques, I* [Paris, 1897], no. 84, pl. 79). Both show the figure wearing a *chiton* beneath the *himation,* as does a cruder statuette in Boston (inv. no. 01.7497; BMFA, *Bronzes*, 53, no. 54, ill.). The exposed right breast of the Watkins piece is extremely unusual in a figure of mid-fifth-century date, leading Hanfmann to assert that the goddess herself is represented, not a mere devotee. A slightly later mirror figure from Magna Graecia, in Hamburg (inv. no. 1963, 15; H. Hoffmann, "Erwerbungen der Antikenabteilung 1961-1963," *Jahrbuch der Hamburger Kunstsammlungen,* 8 [1963], 209-211), also shows the breast exposed and shares with the Fogg Aphrodite a consciousness of the spiral play of heavy drapery and of the forms of the body beneath the garment. A second mirror support from Locri, in the museum at Reggio Calabria (Charbonneaux, *Bronzes*, pl. 21:2), depicts a male figure but shows a similar feel for the draping of cloth and for revealing an organic body beneath it.

Hanfmann points out that these characteristics of the Watkins piece, in addition to its somewhat awkward angularity, are at odds with the columnar severity of the contemporary *peplos*-clad female figures from caryatid mirrors, generally considered to be Corinthian. He there-fore rejects Schuchhardt's localization of the master's workshop in Corinth, defining the style as "based on Peloponnesian formulae [with] peculiar stylistic deviations," possible due to a mixture of Doric and Ionian influences (*AJA,* 284).

The iron pin in the head remains unexplained. Microscopic examination makes it clear that it was tapped down in antiquity, not cut or broken off in modern times. It has been suggested that the figure was originally planned as a handle for a caryatid mirror or vessel. Although iconographically the goddess of love and beauty is ideally suited for representation on a mirror handle, this statuette is freer than most such figures and is intended to be viewed in the round, rather than frontally. Furthermore, mirror figures were usually cast in one piece with the attachment member to which the mirror disk was joined. Even if this were not done, no parallel suggests that an iron rather than a bronze joining pin would have been used.

SD

Bibliography: FAM Acquisitions 1959-62, 31, ill.; G.M.A. Hanfmann, "An Early Classical Aphrodite," *AJA,* 66 (1962), 281-284, pls. 73-74; idem, *Classical Sculpture* (Greenwich, Conn., 1967), 318, no. 143, and fig. 143; Fogg, *Master Bronzes,* 97, no. 93, ill., and 11, fig. 5; R.M. Organ, "The Conservation of Bronze Objects," in *Art and Technology,* 80, fig. 9; H. Hoffman, *Collecting Greek Antiquities* (New York, 1971), 71, fig. 63. Cf. E. Langlotz, "Bermerkungen zu einem Basaltkopf in München," *JdI,* 61-62 (1946-1947), 95-111; W. H. Schuchhardt, "Köpfe des strengen Stils," in *Festschrift für Carl Weickert* (Berlin, 1955), 59-73.

 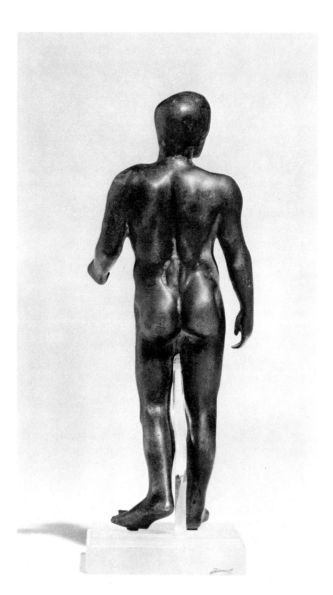

7

Standing Youth

Greek, South Italian, ca. 450-440 B.C.

Bronze, H. 4⅝ in. (0.118 m.)

Solid cast. Dull metallic patina; projecting parts are a lighter metallic color. Rectangular patch in l. shoulder. Seam (?) around upper l. thigh; seam in back of neck. L. foot bent slightly upward; index finger on r. hand bent downward. Both feet rest on sole-shaped platforms and preserve stubs of tangs in heels for insertion into a base. R. hand is a crude wedge of metal, with fingers defined only by incision. Hollow eyes may once have been inlaid in silver.

Provenance: A. Emmerich Gallery, 1970, to Frederick M. Watkins; Bequest to the Fogg Art Museum, Harvard University, 1972.328.

The artist has caught the youth with his head turned and mouth open as if about to speak. Perhaps he is in the act of pouring a libation. The blocky, sharply defined musculature and *contrapposto* stance of this little athlete make him a variation upon the type created by Polykleitos, the master bronzecaster who defined the sculptural ideal for the nude athletic figure around 450 B.C. Some features of the Watkins athlete, however, such as the broad back muscles, the diamond-shaped depression in the spine just above the hips, and the smaller indentations in the outer sides of the buttocks, suggest that the artist who cast it had not yet achieved a totally harmonious integration of motion and anatomy.

Although called a Roman adaptation of the *Doryphoros* of Polykleitos in the Emmerich catalogue, the statuette avoids the heaviness and academic precision of many Roman Imperial copies and versions in bronze of Polykleitan models (e.g. Hermes in Boston and one in the Royal Ontario Museum, Toronto, BMFA, *Bronzes,* 104-105, no. 110, ill.; Fogg, *Master Bronzes,* 257, no. 247, ill.). The inconsistencies in modeling, the bull-like head with cap of hair and prominent sideburns, and the poorly executed hands are consistent with features observable in western Greek bronze statuettes produced during the first half of the fifth century B.C. The Polykleitan structure of the torso, combined with traits retained from the Severe Style, is also characteristic of bronzes from Magna Graecia, such as the "Adrano Boy," in Syracuse (Langlotz, *S. Italy,* pls. 84-85, pl. X). It is not unlikely that the Watkins statuette was produced in one of the major Greek cities of southern Italy (Tarentum, Lokri, Kroton, or possibly Paestum) around the middle of the fifth century B.C. or slightly later.

DGM

Bibliography: A. Emmerich Gallery, *Art of Ancient Italy* (New York, 1968), 62-63, no. 103.

8

Open-Faced Helmet

Greek, ca. 500 B.C.

Bronze, H. 9½ in. (0.243 m.); W. 6⅞ in. (0.173 m.);
D. 8⅞ in. (0.228 m.)

Hammered. Light green patina with spots of reddish cuprite throughout. Some slight modern repairs visible on front of crest area. Chip broken out of forward edge of l. cheek piece.

Provenance: Sale, London, Sotheby, November 14, 1966, to Frederick M. Watkins; Bequest to the Fogg Art Museum, Harvard University, 1972.55.

This helmet provides an open rectangular area exposing the face of its wearer (W. at top 3½ in. [0.09 m.]; W. at bottom 2⅝ in. [0.068 m.]), flanked by two cheek guards with vertical front edges. Front and back edges of the guards are outlined by an incised groove, which expands into tangs projecting laterally from the upper corners of the open area. There is a perforation near the tip of each guard, perhaps for securing a chin strap or leather lining. Another perforation in the helmet just below the beginning of the ridges along the crest may have held a pin to fasten a rosette or other ornament. Two raised parallel ridges run backward along the crest of the helmet. On either side of these are raised oval areas terminating in thinner forked ridges curving backward, perhaps representing stylized snakes' heads. A projecting flange (W. 1½ in. [0.019 m.]) protected the back of the wearer's head and the nape of his neck.

Helmets of this form, most abundant as dedications at Olympia during the seventh and sixth centuries B.C., have also been found with some frequency as grave offerings in Epirus, Macedonia, and adjacent regions of southern Yugoslavia and Albania. E. Kunze has traced the formal and technical development of the type ("Der sogenannte illyrische Helm," *Olympia Bericht,* 6[1958], 125-151). Originally, it was fashioned in two halves fastened down the center, as were the elaborate Cretan helmets of the late seventh century B.C. (H. Hoffmann, *Early Cretan Armourers* [Mainz, 1972], 17-18). Later made in one piece, these helmets became increasingly light and graceful. A. M. Snodgrass considers the type a Peloponnesian invention that later spread and persisted throughout northern Greece and the Balkans (*Early Greek Armour and Weapons* [Edinburgh, 1964], 18-20).

Close in form to the Watkins helmet are the following: 1) a helmet in the National Museum, dated late sixth century B.C. (P. Amandry, *Collection Hélène Stathatos: Les Bijoux Antiques* [Strasbourg, 1953], 50, no. 111, pl. 20); 2) one on the art market dated ca. 500 B.C. (*Ars Antiqua Auktion IV* [Luzern, December 7, 1962], no. 119, pl. 39); 3) Walters Art Gallery, inv. no. 54.2456 (D. K. Hill, "Helmet and Mask and a North Greek Burial," *Journal of the Walters Art Gallery,* 27-28 [1964-65], 9-15; also *Archaeology,* 18 [1965], 64, ill.); 4) Mainz, Römisch-Germanischen Zentralmuseum (inv. no. 0.34890; F. J. Hassel, "Ein archaischer Grabfund von der Chalkidike," *Jahrbuch der Römisch-Germanisches Zentralmuseum,* 14 [1967], 204, pl. 55). The helmet once on the Swiss art market also displays the stylized snakes' heads in relief flanking the crest. These parallels suggest that the Watkins helmet belongs to the northern Greek branch of the open-faced helmet and may be dated ca. 500 B.C.

DGM

Bibliography: Sotheby Sale Catalogue (London, November 14, 1966), lot 175. I am grateful to Dorothy Kent Hill for information about the helmets in Baltimore and Mainz and for bibliographical references.

9

Attachment with Bovine Head

Greek, 3rd to 2nd century B.C.

Bronze, H. 4⁵⁄₁₆ in. (0.11 m.); W. 3³⁄₁₆ in. (0.082 m.); H. of head 2⅛ in. (0.055 m.)

Cast in one piece; head hollow. Intact. Extensive iron oxide accretion between horns removed in 1967 by Fogg Conservation Department. Uneven edge of neck and imperfections at base of upright rod suggest casting flaws.

Provenance: Charles L. Morley to Frederick M. Watkins, 1963; Gift to the Fogg Art Museum, Harvard University, 1964.145.

A massive, sensitively modeled bovine head protrudes from three tangent rings with a vertical rod passing behind them. The heavy head has a wide muzzle with crescentic nostrils, small eyes peering from beneath pronounced lids and brow ridges, and stumpy curving horns. The ears are deeply hollowed. The shaggy hair between the horns is disposed in small rounded tufts, each subdivided into two or three curving locks. The rings, circular in section, show no trace of attachment to something larger.

Although this unusual bronze has no immediate parallels, the triangular group of rings recalls the three wing- or lobe-like plates by which cast bull-head protomes were riveted onto the shoulders of bronze cauldrons from Urartu during the eighth century B.C. (cf. cauldron from Altintepe, now in Ankara; E. Akurgal, *Die Kunst Anatoliens* [Berlin, 1961], 54, figs. 30-32). A number of smaller, cruder objects featuring a bull's head superimposed on three circles are known from Anatolia. Although none has yet been found in controlled excavation, they appear to be Roman in date (cf. BMFA, *Bronzes,* 280-281, nos. 404-405, ill.). They may have been used as harness or furniture attachments, small votive objects, or pendants.

Various uses for the Watkins bronze have been suggested. In a letter to Watkins of November 1, 1963, Morley repeats G. M. A. Richter's theory that it is an attachment for a throne or other piece of furniture and E. Bielefeld's suggestion of its use as part of a ceremonial cart or chariot *(Kultwagen)* of the Argive Hera. If the latter is the case, the upright rod would have been inserted into the railing, with the rings serving as rein guides and, according to Bielefeld, the head would be that of a cow, not a bull. In the absence of convincing parallels, these explanations must remain tentative.

Dating, likewise, is elusive; the sympathetic, organic modeling and the plastic treatment of the tufts of hair render a Roman date unlikely. The absence of baroque treatment with accompanying emotional overtones strengthens the relationship to the classical tradition of the fourth century B.C. The bronze would be most at home in a milieu that continued these traditions into the third and early second centuries B.C. West-central Asia Minor seems most congenial, although Athens and the Peloponnesus would also provide such circumstances.
DGM

Bibliography: D. G. Mitten, "A Bronze Bull Protome," *FAM Acquisitions, 1965,* 136-140, ill.; Fogg, *Master Bronzes,* 141, no. 145, ill.

10

Gorgon Head

Greek, Sicilian or South Italian, ca. 530 B.C.

Terra cotta, H. 4 in. (0.103 m.); W. 2¹⁵⁄₁₆ in. (0.075 m.)

Fine brown clay. Mold-made; features sharpened and
retouched with a pointed tool. Back hollow, showing
finger marks left in smoothing. Lower l. curls and l. ear
broken off.

Provenance: Frederick M. Watkins; Gift to the Fogg Art
Museum, Harvard University, 1959.194.

This unusual Gorgon mask demonstrates the effects that a
craftsman could obtain by modeling and refining a mold-
made impression with tools. The mask is too small to have
served as an antefix or other architectural terra cotta, yet
is larger than the mold-made heads for most votive figurines or plastic vases. It may have come from an *arula*
(cf. No. 11) or have been an appliqué for a krater or hydria
that imitated in terra cotta the intricate figurative handle
attachments and other ornaments of metal vessels (cf. Corinthian column krater, National Museum, Copenhagen,
Chr. VIII 940; M. Gjφdesen, "Greek Bronzes: A Review
Article," *AJA,* 67[1963], pl. 76, fig. 39 [horses], pl. 78,
fig. 44 [reclining satyr]).

DGM

Bibliography: Unpublished. Compare the painted terra
cotta plaque with gorgon in Syracuse, and the plastic
curls on terra cottas from Megara Hyblaea and Agrigento
(Langlotz, *S. Italy,* 243, frontispiece, pl. 1; pl. 5, right;
244-245, pl. 6).

II

Arula

Greek, Sicilian or South Italian, ca. 510-490 B.C.

Terra cotta, H. 7 in. (0.18 m.); L. 13¾ in. (0.35 m.);
D. 5⅞ in. (0.15 m.); wall thickness 1½ in. (0.035 m.);
interior: L. 11⅜ in. (0.29 m.); W. 3⅞ in. (0.10 m.);
H. 5¼ in. (0.135 m.)

Tan, porous clay with large particles of brick-red grog.
Mold-made relief. Yellow-gray calcium carbonate deposit
obscures surface. Much of top and bottom profiles broken.
No trace of fire or other sacrificial use on top.

Provenance: Dr. Philip Lederer, Berlin, to Charles L.
Morley; to Frederick M. Watkins, 1963; Bequest to the
Fogg Art Museum, Harvard University, 1972.48.

This rectangular *arula,* or small altar, has concave sides
and simple projecting profiles at top and bottom. On the
top left profile are two squares of meander. The front
shows, under an arching vine, a silen walking to the right,
looking back, with a tall-handled kantharos in his extended right hand and a branch in his left. He is followed
by a horse carrying a maenad and a small silen or satyr. His
right foot is human, his left equine or incomplete. The
maenad, dressed in an overgirt *chiton* rather than the
customary tight *peplos,* seems to drop the reins from her
raised left hand as she glides off the horse. Her bent right
arm is intertwined with the left arm of a small satyr, who
clutches the tail of the horse with his right hand. He has
a short, erect penis. The horse, with arching neck, paws
the ground as a cheetah passes under his nose, chasing a
hare that looks back over its shoulder.

The function of *arulae* is still under discussion. Not all
of them seem to have been actually used as altars. The
style and material of this example bear out Morley's
allegation of a Sicilian or South Italian provenance. No
exact parallel to the subject seems to occur among terra-
cotta reliefs.

The iconographic features and sprightliness of the
representation are in the Ionian tradition; the "Caeretan
hydriai," ca. 530-520 B.C., offer precedents for quick,
angular motion of small figures, for long-bodied horses,
for dashing hares. The maenad gliding from her mount is
related to the Europa on the Castellani hydria, no. 414.

The general figure style is transitional from late
archaic to early classical, parallel to drawings by Attic
late black-figure and early red-figure masters. Compare,
for example, the monumental stance of the walking silen
with the Perithoos by Euthymides; for the enframing
arbor compare that of the Andokides Painter's Herakles
(E. Pfuhl, *Malerei und Zeichnung der Griechen* [Munich,
1923], fig. 369; fig. 315).
GMAH and JCW

Bibliography: Unpublished. We have drawn on a prelim-
inary unpublished study by P. Gerstenblith, "An Archaic
Arula in the Fogg Museum," (1972). On shape and function of *arulae,* cf. E. D. Van Buren, "Terracotta Arulae,"
MAAR, 2 (1918), 15-54; 5, 27 (sileni), and most recently,
P. Orlandini, "Arule archaiche a rilievo nel Museo
Nazionale di Gela," *RM,* 66 (1959), 97-103, pls. 28-32;
A. De Franciscis, "Monasterace Marina Caulonia," *NSc,*
11 (1957), 184-186, fig. 1 (shape), fig. 4 (silen with
amphora); A. Adriani and E. Joly, *Himera* 1 (Rome, 1970),
214, 295, 385, figs. 23, 25, pls. 63:3, 65:3. On "Caeretan
hydriai," cf. T. B. L. Webster, "A Rediscovered Caeretan
Hydria," *JHS,* 48 (1928), 196-205, fig. 3, pls. 12-13; P.
Mingazzini, *Vasi della Collezione Castellani* (Rome, 1950),
175, pl. 39:1; P. E. Arias and B. Shefton, *Greek Vase
Painting* (New York, 1961), 311-313, figs. 77, 79, 80;
J. M. Hemelrijk, *De Caeretaanse Hydriae* (Rotterdam,
1956), 110, no. 5.

Antefix: Head of a Satyr

Greek, South Italian, probably Tarentine, ca. 500 B.C.

Terra cotta, H. 7¼ in. (0.185 m.); W. 5¾ in. (0.145 m.)

Fine-grained, pale pink-beige clay. Broken at both sides and upper r. White slip on back. Substantial pigment remains: salmon-pink on flesh, black on beard and irises of eyes, deep magenta on hair, yellow ochre on chin-whiskers.

Provenance: A. Emmerich Gallery to Frederick M. Watkins; Bequest to the Fogg Art Museum, Harvard University, 1972.326.

This antefix was originally a semicircular plaque that capped the end of a cover tile *(kalypter)* shaped like a section of pipe divided in half longitudinally. The *kalypteres* were used to cover the vertical seams where two flat roof tiles abutted, and served to make the roof more watertight. Their outer ends were decorated with brightly-painted antefixes, usually—as here—showing a single frontal head that dominates the entire field (see also No. 13).

The satyr's head has been reduced here to a symmetrical, highly stylized pattern in very low relief. Hair and beard form a continuous arc, echoing the semicircle of the plaque. The hair is treated as a series of parallel furrows. The beard is composed of an inner band of long narrow triangles in yellow ochre and three outer curving rows of broader triangles in black. The eyes are elongated, the moustache attenuated and curving modishly downward. These features show the influence of Ionian models. The over-all effect is sleepily serene and unemotional, an abstract decorative pattern that stands in striking contrast to the agitated, exaggerated features of the antefix from Gela (No. 13).

Several other terra cottas are extremely close to this one, suggesting that they may have been made from the same one-piece mold or at least have been based on the same model. They are in the Museo Nazionale, Tarentum, Ny Carlsberg Glyptothek (inv. no. 1006; found at Tarentum), and Budapest (Tarentine; said to come from Cumae). A related type, also from Tarentum, shares with this piece the broad, flat features and drooping moustache, while lacking its subtly pervasive sense of patterning. (Examples are Trieste, inv. no. 15; Cleveland Museum of Art, inv. no. 26.552.) A slightly more distant relative, said only to come from Italy, was in the Loeb Collection (J. Sieveking, *Die Terrakotten der Sammlung Loeb,* 2 [Munich, 1916], 60, pl. 118).

Despite the archaic cast of the features, the sophisticated stylization of the antefix suggests a date at the turn of the century.

SD

Bibliography: Unpublished. For the Tarentum Museum piece: C. Laviosa, "Le antefisse fittile di Taranto," *ArchCl,* 6 (1954), 243-244, no. 39, pl. 76:1, with bibl. for pieces in Copenhagen and Budapest as well as for two others not known to this author. For the Trieste piece: P. Wuilleumier, *Tarente, des origines à la conquête romaine, Bibliothèque des Ecoles Françaises d'Athènes et de Rome,* fasc. 148 (Paris, 1939), 426-427, pl. 38:7, with bibl. for piece in Cleveland.

35

13

Antefix: Head of a Satyr

Greek, Sicilian, probably from Gela, ca. 470-450 B.C.

Terra cotta, H. 9¼ in. (0.235 m.); W. 7⅞ in. (0.20 m.)

Rather coarse pinkish clay with large inclusions, up to ¼ in. in diam., of red ochre (iron oxide) and other iron compounds. Clay also contains volcanic sand, perhaps added to strengthen the fabric. Head has been broken into two pieces and mended; seam runs through beard at level of lower cheek and through mouth. Modern plaster and clay infill at join. Chips along outer edge of hair and beard. Some erosion of surface on ears, eyebrows, eyes, lips. Irregular edge at back of head suggests the head was broken from a more extensive architectural member (see below). Surface covered with thick greenish-white slip, in which brush marks can be seen. Traces of white pigment on eyeballs; white and red in rim around eyes; red on folds of skin around eyes, r. cheek, r. ear.

Provenance: Charles L. Morley to Frederick M. Watkins, 1961; Bequest to the Fogg Art Museum, Harvard University, 1972.49.

This expressive satyr probably served as an antefix, decorating the lateral cornice of a building (see No. 12). Such heads, with open mouths, also were positioned at the edge of the roof gutters to provide drainage, much as did gargoyles later on Gothic cathedrals. Because of the angle at which they were set, the heads directed rain water away from the rather friable limestone of which buildings were usually made in Greek Sicily. The modern repair of this satyr makes it difficult to determine whether its mouth was originally open or closed.

A number of virtually identical satyrs' heads have been excavated at Gela. They are thought to have adorned a *thesauros* or similar secondary religious building in the modern Via Apollo. Orlandini has divided these into three types; the Fogg piece falls into his Group A, owing to its heavy sausage-like eyebrows and the pattern of the furrows in its forehead. There are minor differences: less pronounced modeling of the lips, lack of the small spade-shaped goatee over the arc of chin-whiskers, less elaboration of the moustache, and an apparent absence of teeth. All these could be accounted for by differences in tooling the leather-hard clay after its removal from the mold and before firing. Like the satyrs from the Via Apollo, the Fogg

piece seems to have been formed in one piece with the roof-tile *(kalypter)* from which it projected. The beginning of the tile is still preserved behind the head.

The building in the Via Apollo seems to have set quite a fashion in ancient Gela. Related satyrs' heads have been found in another part of the town and in the environs, indicating that the type was widely imitated locally. It is not known outside the immediate vicinity, however. Although satyrs as antefixes were not uncommon in sixth-century Greece and her colonies (cf. No. 12), and although the tradition lived on in Etruria, nowhere but in Gela have satyr antefixes of this vigorously sculptural type been found. Stratigraphic evidence, as well as the Severe Style features of the heads, have suggested a date in the second quarter of the fifth century B.C.

The mythical satyr, representing an amalgam of animal and human qualities, intrigued the Greeks. Over the centuries Greek representations of satyrs became increasingly less bestial, evolving finally into a sort of philosopher type, bereft of ass's ears, hoofs, tail, or other such animal traits. This satyr stands at the fulcrum of the development. Although his pointed ears, bulb nose, bony cranium, and sensuous full lips emphasize the animal aspect of his nature, the artist has imposed a degree of formality, symmetry, and abstraction on the features, particularly on the encircling nimbus of hair and beard, that lend the head a compensatory measure of serenity and rationality. The bold chiaroscuro effect would have been heightened by vivid coloring.

SD

Bibliography: Unpublished. On the Gela series see B. Neutsch, "Archäologische Grabungen und Funde in Sizilien von 1949-1954," *AA* (1954), 659, fig. 104; P. Orlandini, "Le nuove antefisse seleniche di Gela," *ArchCl,* 6 (1954), 251-266, figs. 1, 4; idem, "Gela," *NSc,* 10 (1956), 229-236, figs. 1-8; L. von Matt, *Das Antike Sizilien* (Zürich, 1959), pl. 95; Langlotz, *S. Italy,* 261, pl. 33; P. Griffo and L. von Matt, *Gela* (Greenwich, Conn., 1968), 126, 130, fig. 93.

14

Doll

Greek, Attic, ca. 460-440 B.C.

Terra cotta, H. 5⅞ in. (0.151 m.); W. across shoulders
2½ in. (0.065 m.)

Buff clay, covered with white slip, which has flaked away
in places (l. eye; over much of headdress). Narrow stripes
of black paint around headdress and as a strap passing
over l. shoulder.

Provenance: Frederick M. Watkins; Gift to the Fogg Art
Museum, Harvard University, 1959.192.

This doll is a fine representative of a group of terra cottas
studied by B. Schweitzer ("Eine attische Tonpuppe," *RM,*
44 [1929], 1-25), and by J. Dörig ("Von griechische
Puppen," *AntK,* 1 (1958), 41-52; cf. also H. Kyreleis, in
Antiken aus dem Akademischen Kunstmuseum, Bonn
[Düsseldorf, 1969], no. 58; 50-51, pl. 37). The type, with its
limbs cut off just below the shoulders and hips, seems to be
characteristically Attic, in contrast to the jointed dolls from
the Corinth region (e.g. A. N. Stillwell, *Corinth XV:2, The
Potters' Quarter, The Terracottas* [Princeton, 1952],
145-151, pl. 31). Stillwell dates the Attic class to the third
quarter of the fifth century B.C. (p. 148); however, the
solid forms of the face of the Watkins doll and the
proportions of her headdress could date well before the
middle of the century.

The Watkins doll, like others, wears an upswept,
pointed *sakkos* (kerchief-tied headdress). Children on
Attic grave reliefs of the early fourth century B.C. sometimes hold similar dolls (cf. Fogg Art Museum, 1961.86;
J. G. Pedley, "An Attic Grave Stele in the Fogg Art
Museum," *HSCP,* 69 [1965], 259-268, pls. 1-5; Stillwell,
148, no. 28, cites other examples). Is this a child's toy,
in our sense of the word, or a particular kind of funerary
figurine intended to accompany a child in its grave?

The Watkins doll also effectively illustrates the advanced sculptural rendering of the nude female figure that
Greek artists were able to achieve around the middle of
the fifth century B.C.

DGM

Bibliography: Unpublished.

15

Plastic Alabastron

Greek, Rhodian, "Cypriote Series," ca. 575-560 B.C.

H. 10¼ in. (0.260 m.); Diam. 2 in. (0.051 m.)

Mold-made. Most of surface burnished or smoothed with a small piece of wood or other tool. Intact; vertical crack in upper r. front side; chip from r. side of mouth. Red pigment adheres to top of mouth. Calcium carbonate incrustation on l. back, l. arm.

Provenance: Münzen und Medaillen A. G. to Frederick M. Watkins, 1962; Bequest to the Fogg Art Museum, Harvard University, 1972.47.

The alabastron, a perfume vase, takes its name from the bag-shaped stone ointment vases originally made in Egypt and later imitated in stone, glass, faience, and ceramic all over the eastern Mediterranean during the seventh and sixth centuries B.C.

The upper part of the elegant Watkins alabastron is an enigmatically smiling female form. The extremely crisp details of her facial features, surrounded by a cape-like veil, and her jewelry, especially the beads and central pendant in her necklace, indicate that a fresh mold must have been employed. In her right hand, held stiffly across her breast, she cradles a bird; her left arm hangs at her side. The overall impression she conveys is similar to that of monumental Ionian *korai* of ca. 570-560 B.C. found at Samos and elsewhere.

Although the technique and fabric of the Watkins vase are common to many groups of plastic vases manufactured on Rhodes during the first half of the sixth century, it falls within the Rhodian class termed by Ducat the "Cypriote Series" because of their resemblance to Cypriote sculpture of the sixth century B.C. (pp. 72-74). Ducat lists nine examples, of which ours, no. 8, is one of the finest; to these, add a less precisely molded specimen included in Münzen und Medaillen A. G., *Auktion 34* (Basel, May 6, 1967), 52, no. 110, pl. 28. Ducat also lists prototypes in alabaster, which have been divided by other scholars into two groups: Eastern Mediterranean and Etruscan (cf. P. J. Riis, "Sculptured Alabastra," *ActaA,* 27 [1956], 23-33; S. Haynes, "An Etruscan Alabastron," *AntK,* 6 [1963], 3-5). Ducat (p. 87) places the appearance of the "Cypriote Series" of ceramic alabastra near the beginning of the second quarter of the sixth century B.C.; hence a date ca. 575-560 B.C. is indicated for the Watkins piece.

DGM

Bibliography: Münzen und Medaillen A.G., *Liste E, 120 Antike Terrakotten* (Basel, August 1962), 17, no. 41; J. Ducat, *Les vases plastiques rhodiens archaïques en terre cuite* (Paris, 1966), 73, no. 8.

Column Krater

Greek, Corinthian, ca. 585-575 B.C.

H. 14½ in. (0.368 m.); Diam. at handle plates 16¼ in. (0.41 m.); Diam. of rim 12¼ in. (0.312 m.); Diam. of foot 6⅞ in. (0.174 m.)

Recomposed from fragments. Some losses to head and upper body of l. horseman; missing are forehead of center horse, head and shoulders of r. horseman, part of r. horse's neck. White paint worn or missing in many areas. Interior and rim show abrasion.

Incision widely used for details in black areas: Side A – between couches and banqueters, arms of banqueters, linear decoration of bird on shield; Side B – bridles, manes, tails, eyes of horses, riders' faces and arms, wings and tail of bird; Handle zones – linear decoration of wings, legs, tails of birds; Handle plates – beard-lines, hair, eyes, eyebrows. Red: Side A – himation of r. banqueter, tops of l. and r. footstools, part of l. couch; Side B – bands on wings of bird, on flanks of l. and r. horses, riders' garments; Handle zones – stripes on wings and tails of griffin-birds; every fourth tongue on shoulder; ground line under scenes; stripes above and below wide black band on lower body; band inside mouth of vase. White: Side A – fields of shields, tables, chitons of banqueters, some rounded food items; Side B – center horse; every fourth tongue on shoulder.

Provenance: A. Emmerich Gallery to Frederick M. Watkins, 1968; to the Fogg Art Museum, Harvard University, Gift of Frederick M. Watkins and Purchase from the David M. Robinson Fund, 1968.13.

Side A: *Symposium*
Side B: *Cavalcade*
Handle zone: *Griffin-birds*
Handle plates: *Bearded male busts in profile*

The column krater, which affords two large horizontal panels for decoration, was particularly favored for the monumental compositions of Late Corinthian vase-painters. Their creations probably reflect large-scale paintings on walls and on terra-cotta plaques that have not survived. The most common format was to compose each side in a tripartite scheme. Here three galloping horsemen are countered by a trio of bearded banqueters in repose.

The pale Corinthian clay has been painted with orange slip before decoration, in deliberate imitation of the reddish fabric of Attic pottery. Vases with such a slip treatment have been found primarily at Caere (ancient Cervetri) in Etruria; at this period Corinthians and Athenians were ruthlessly competing for the lucrative Etruscan export market, which the Corinthians were soon to lose.

The figures are painted in a lustrous brown-black glaze, using both the black-figure silhouette technique, with incised details, and line drawing enclosing areas painted in white. Red-brown joins black and white in the tongue motif on the vessel's shoulder.

Both figural scenes are part of the stock repertoire of the Late Corinthian vase-painter—treated here with great vitality, if somewhat summarily. The banqueters engage in lively conversation from their couches. Before them stand three-legged tables bearing cups and plates of food. The fugitive white pigment in which the tables were rendered has almost vanished. Footstools rest under the couches, while on the wall above are hung the warriors' fillets and their shields, decorated with the bucranium (bull's head), flying bird, and serpent.

The bold overlapping of horses on Side B contrasts with the parataxis of the symposiasts, revealing the painter's command of this device for indicating spatial recession. Horseback races were part of the Olympic and other Pan-hellenic games at this time but may also have been connected with funerary rites. Similarly, the banquet may connote either a celebration or a funeral. It is likely that this vase, like most of its fellows, eventually came to rest in the tomb of its Etruscan owner.

The mythical griffin-birds beneath the handles do not relate to the adjacent scenes but are vestiges of the animal friezes popular in earlier Corinthian vase painting. Profile heads are common on the handle plates of kraters of this type, but their significance is unclear.

Nonsense inscriptions occur on both sides of the vase. They were probably included as filling ornament, much as were rosettes and dots on earlier Corinthian vases; alternatively, they may have imitated the careful name-labels of more elaborate Greek productions, to the satisfaction of the Etruscan buyer who presumably did not read Greek.

The vase has been designated (Emmerich catalogue) as "near the late work of the Detroit Painter." J. L. Benson (by letter) connects it generally with his "Group of the White Horses," being reluctant to place it more precisely because of the lack of an identifying animal frieze. One might compare a krater with similar scenes in Boston (inv. no. 01.8040; Benson, *Geschichte*, 58, list 101, no. 1).

SD

Bibliography: A. Emmerich Gallery, *Art of the Ancients* (New York, 1968), 6-7, no. 3, ill.; D. G. Mitten and S. Doeringer, "A Corinthian Krater in the Fogg Art Museum," *FAM Acquisitions, 1968*, 33-43, figs. 1-4. On Detroit Painter see D. Amyx, "The Medallion Painter," *AJA,* 65 (1961), no. 31; J. L. Benson, "The Three Maidens Group," *AJA,* 73 (1969), 114-115. On "Gruppe der weissen Pferde," J. L. Benson, *Die Geschichte der Korinthischen Vasen* (Basel, 1953), 58-59, list 101, and P. Bocci, "A Corinthian Oinochoe in the Archaeological Museum in Florence," *AJA,* 74 (1970), 97-98.

17

Black-Figure Panel Amphora (Type B)

Greek, Attic, attributed to Group E [Beazley], ca. 550-530 B.C.

H. 17 in. (0.432 m.)

Broken and repaired; missing pieces restored and painted. Red: Side A – Herakles' *chiton*, edge of lion skin, Eurytion's beard and *chiton*, Geryon's greaves, helmets, shield rims, Orthros's ruff; Side B – men's hair, two beards, parts of drapery, woman's hair, parts of *peplos*; cuffs of palmettes, frames of panels, edges of base and mouth.

Provenance: Jacob Hirsch; Sale, Paris, Hôtel Drouot, June 30-July 2, 1921; Frederick M. Watkins; Bequest to the Fogg Art Museum, Harvard University, 1972.42.

Side A: *Herakles and Geryon*
Side B: *Arming*

Side A shows Herakles, dressed in lion skin over *chitoniskos*, fighting Geryon, the triple-bodied monster who lived in regions farthest west and was rich in cattle (Apollodoros, *Bibliotheke,* ii.v.10). Herakles was sent to fetch the cattle at his tenth labor and succeeded in killing not only Geryon's herdsman Eurytion, shown fallen at Herakles' feet, but also the monster's two-headed dog Orthros, at Geryon's feet, and Geryon himself. Geryon is conceived as having three bodies joined at the waist. Each wears greaves and a high-crested Corinthian helmet (two are visible; the top of the third is partly hidden), and each carries a shield.

Side B shows a man arming before spectators. In the center the man puts on a greave; at his feet is his Corinthian helmet. On either side are spectators: to the left, a man in *himation* and a man in *chiton* and *himation;* to the right, a woman in *peplos* and a nude man. Above the scene on Side A is a palmette festoon; on Side B, a palmette chain; at the base are rays.

Group E is the name given by Beazley to "a large and compact group which is very closely related to the work of the painter Exekias, though earlier . . ., the soil from which the art of Exekias springs" (*ABV,* 133). The battle of Herakles and Geryon is one of their favorite subjects and is found on at least nine other amphorae with much the same composition. Compare Würzburg 245 (E. Langlotz, *Griechische Vasen in Würzburg* [Munich, 1932], pl. 79), where the drawing is neater, the shepherd Eurytion is partly fallen, and the dog Orthros is missing.

DB

Bibliography: Hôtel Drouot, *Collection Hirsch* (Paris, June 30-July 2, 1921), 20, no. 141, pl. 6; *ABV,* 133, no. 8; Buitron, *Attic Vases,* 28-29, no. 10.

18

Black-Figure Oinochoe

Greek, Attic, ca. 500-480 B.C.

H. 8⅞ in. (0.226 m.); Diam. of body ca. 5¼ in. (0.135 m.)

Intact, except for chip from r. side of spout. Purple: maenads' garlands, stripes and dots on their clothing, teats and circular stripes on pantheress. White: maenads' faces, arms and feet (applied over black), stripe down pantheress's face, tiny groups of three dots on maenads' costumes.

Provenance: Frederick M. Watkins; Gift to the Fogg Art Museum, Harvard University, 1959.189.

In its thin, precisely crimped trefoil spout and its handle, marked by a ridge down the center, this oinochoe (wine pitcher) betrays a metallic prototype. Vertical borders of a double row of dots enclosed by pairs of lines form the sides of the figured panel; a fringe of closely-spaced tongues radiating from the neck overlaps the top of the panel. Featured in the panel are two lively maenads engaged in a Dionysiac dance, who accompany their performance with *krotala* (elongated bone castanets). A small pantheress, the same size as a modern house cat, cocks its head to one side in response to the movement. The grapevines before which the maenads dance enhance the mood of Dionysiac revelry. Their clusters of grapes are represented by pear-shaped blobs of black paint. The vine stems are bordered by single rows of minute black dots. The drawing and incision are hastily facile but not sloppy. This oinochoe is a representative example of workshop black-figure painting at a time when the most talented artists were increasingly turning to the new, more versatile red-figure technique.

DGM

Bibliography: Unpublished.

19

Red-Figure Kalpis

Greek, Attic, Pioneer Group, 510-500 B.C.

H. 15 in. (0.38 m.); Diam. of foot 5⅞ in. (0.147 m.); Diam. at mouth 6⅛ in. (0.155 m.); Diam. at handles 15 in. (0.38 m.)

Intact, except for one restored side handle, chip from mouth; chip from Hector's cheek and abrasion in front bed leg are miniscule.

Numerous thin preliminary sketch lines indicate bodies under drapery; rear bed leg and table leg were planned farther to r.

Glaze very glossy. Reserved: areas between handles, underside of foot, top of mouth. Interior of neck glazed to depth of 1¼ in. An accident during glazing has caused numerous spots, which stand out clearly against the normal brushed-on glaze. Background perhaps painted by careless assistant, who sometimes ran over motifs and left other small spaces unglazed. Incision: head contours of Achilles and Priam, hair locks of Hector. Relief contour throughout, except for small sections, e.g. Priam's toes, couch, table feet. Head and beard of Hector reserved. Dilute glaze used extensively: large folds in drapery, sleeves of Priam, muscles in all figures. Deeper dilute glaze for blood flowing from Hector's many wounds; shield shading. Red: letters; thin band around neck at upper end of vertical handle; thin bands accenting upper and lower borders of reserved areas behind horizontal handles; hair band of Achilles. A gory detail is the red liquid dripping from the table onto Hector's chest.

Provenance: Münzen und Medaillen A.G. to Frederick M. Watkins, 1967; Bequest to the Fogg Art Museum, Harvard University, 1972.40.

Ransom of Hector

Achilles, reclining on a modest couch, hacks away rudely at his victuals, which seem to be dripping over Priam's dead son, Hector. Priam, in despair and supplication, presses his elderly hands against Achilles' knees. The heroic Hector lies in front of the table, legs bound. The letters, with the exception of ΠΡΙΑΜΟΣ, serve as space fillers (see Buitron, *Attic Vases;* Münzen und Medaillen, *Auktion 34*).

As observed in the Münzen und Medaillen catalogue, the subject is not common; the closest parallel is the kylix by Oltos in Munich (inv. no. 2618; *ARV,* 61, no. 74). There the composition is more suited to the vase; the dead Hector is not over-sized, for he did not, as on the kalpis, need to fill an extended area. On the kylix the banquet meat and vines are explicitly painted. The standing female crowning Achilles on the kylix seems more apt than the helmet-shield group occupying a similar position in the composition on the kalpis. Perhaps the kalpis scene is a shorthand variation of a cup theme. However, the Kleophrades Painter, on a fragmentary calyx krater from the Kerameikos (*ARV,* 186, no. 45), drew an extremely sensitive rendition, to judge from the head of the dead Hector.

To Beazley this kalpis recalls Euthymides and the earliest work of the Kleophrades Painter (*Paralipomena,* 324). The shape was decorated by both, and in like pictorial systems. The full, rounded palmettes of the Fogg kalpis remind one of palmettes on Leningrad 624 (*ARV,* 28, no. 15), Bonn 70 (*ARV,* 28, no. 12), and Vatican G71 (*ARV,* 28, no. 14), but the Fogg border is more lively with its horizontal, eared palmette pairs, separated by leaves. An even richer border is found on the neck of a volute krater by Euthymides from Morgantina (*ARV,* 28, no. 10). Both painters frame their pictures with pomegranates and tongues (cf. Kleophrades Painter kalpis in Basel; *ARV,* 189, no. 73).

The composition here is basically a three-figure group, with the helmet-on-shield as the third standing figure. Three of the four hydrai attributed to Euthymides show this old-fashioned format. Beazley's indecision in attribution is understandable, for the comparisons lie in both directions. The brutal head of Achilles reminds one of the Herakles fragment from the Agora by the Kleophrades Painter (inv. no. P 7241; *ARV,* 189, no. 79), but the drapery has affinities with the reclining figures on the Morgantina krater by Euthymides. Although the helmet and frontal foot find parallels in the work of Euthymides (Munich 2307 and 2309; *ARV,* 26, no. 1 and 27, no. 4), they could as well have been by the Kleophrades Painter. The pleading expression on Priam's face points to Onesimos.

Part of the problem in attribution is the peculiar mixture of careless drawing with fine drawing. For example, compare the clumsy ear of Priam with the neat ear of

Achilles; contrast the beautiful treatment of the dead Hector–his closed eyelids, eyelashes, incised spreading hair and tied feet–with the ugly left hand of Achilles and the unformed fingers of Priam. Note the confusion between Achilles' drapery and the buns, where the glaze was not filled in. The omission of the front table leg below Hector's shoulder and the bed slat below the legs of Achilles are inconsistent with the delicate dilute glaze shading on the shield. At present the kalpis seems more akin to Euthymides than to the Kleophrades Painter.

AHA and KMP

Bibliography: Paralipomena, 324; Münzen und Medaillen A.G., Auktion 34 (Basel, May 6, 1967), 75-76, no. 149, pls. 46-47; Buitron, Attic Vases, 80-81, no. 37.

20

Red-Figure Calyx Krater

Greek, Attic, early work by the Kleophrades Painter,
ca. 500 B.C.

H. 17¼ in. (0.438 m.); Diam. of mouth 20¼ in. (0.515 m.);
Diam. with handles 18⅞ in. (0.48 m.); Diam. of base
10¼ in. (0.26 m.)

Broken and mended; earlier repaint removed; handles
restored.

Numerous single preliminary sketch lines, not heavily
impressed, are hastily drawn. Single lines used to block
in broad areas; they were not intended as final lines over
which black glaze was applied. Lyre-holding satyr to l. of
Dionysos originally may have stood with l. leg far forward, crossing r. leg of Dionysos. This change to a tight,
closed stance resembling a jumper's pose removed the
satyr from impinging on Dionysos's space.

Brilliant glaze throughout; reserved outside are upper and
lower edges of step in foot; reserved inside, three bands
and circle at bottom. Relief contour throughout, except
lower edge of Hephaistos's mallet and the beards, which
are reserved. Heavy hairs along lower borders of beards
are continued into beards, adding texture. Palmettes
contoured but not their hearts. Head and hair contours
incised with scalloped pattern. Heavy glaze dots, applied
against this incision, emphasize curly hair contour. Dots
encircle head contour of satyr with pointed amphora and
outline beard of horn-carrying satyr. Where surface is
intact, extensive dilute glaze lines indicate anatomy.
Thinned glaze: inner satyr ear lines, lines down some
penises, dots on leopard skins. Yellow wash: leopard skins,
wine sacks, shoes, tortoise shell of lyre. Red: ivy wreaths,
fillet, lyre and cithara plectra, cords, tuning pegs, mule's
bridle and lead strap, dots on vine of Dionysos,
inscriptions.

Provenance: Said to come from Tarentum. Jacob Hirsch
to Frederick M. Watkins, 1941; Gift to the Fogg Art
Museum, Harvard University, 1960.236.

Return of Hephaistos

A boisterous procession of ithyphallic satyrs and a mule,
accompanying Dionysos and Hephaistos, encircles the
vase. Each god dominates a side; the end satyrs are skill-
fully posed at the A/B handle, forming a spontaneous
starting and finishing group. Attention is drawn to
Dionysos by the yellow wash on his cloak and on those
of his surrounding satyrs. Hephaistos, on mule-back, is
raised above the melee. Music is provided by two flutes,
a cithara, and a lyre; ample wine, brought in two goat
skins and a pointed amphora, will go into the hefty volute
krater. Only one satyr holds a drinking horn; Dionysos
has his own kantharos. The inscriptions are nonsense. The
scene swells out of its space into the upper border;
Hephaistos almost vanishes into a palmette.

The picture is bordered above by a band of encircled
palmettes and below by a key pattern. A tongue band runs
around the body above the foot. Two bands frame the top
and bottom of the tongues outside. The eighth-inch strip
is very pronounced.

There are many tiny, exquisite technical details. The
handles, rim, and base of the bowl of the kantharos were
reserved. Note also the reserved teeth of the mallet-
wielding satyr, the dots at the top of the kantharos stem,
the claws on the leopard skins, and the reserved moustache
of the first flutist on Side A. The wine sack carried by the
flutist on Side B is especially fine. The goat hair is drawn,
almost like feathers, with rows of dots alternating with
long vertical strokes. The left-side markings were regular
(perhaps for smoothed hair), the right irregular (perhaps
for windblown hair).

G. M. A. Richter attributes the vase to the Kleophrades
Painter and proves that two closely related psykters
(Louvre G57 and Compiegne 1068; *ARV*, 188, no. 65 and
no. 66) must also be by his hand. In her astute analysis she
enumerates the early stylistic characteristics of the painter,
"a pupil of Euthymides, who in his early days closely
imitated his master's style."

The Fogg krater is far superior to the psykters in its
lively, robust drawing. Hephaistos might be more effective
if his head were not lost in the border.

AHA and KMP

Bibliography: G. M. A. Richter, "The Kleophrades
Painter," *AJA,* 40 (1936), 100-115, photographed with
restorations; Fogg, *Ancient Art,* 35, no. 273, pl. 81; *ARV,*
185, no. 31.

21

Red-Figure Kylix (Type B)

Greek, Attic, painted by Makron, ca. 490-480 B.C.

H. 4⅞ in. (0.122 m.); Diam. 12¾ in. (0.325 m.)
(dimensions and photograph before restoration)

Assembled from many pieces; damage at all breaks, some filled during early repair. Int: loss of surface, worst at center; satyr scratched; glaze and dilute glaze lines lost; missing are satyr's nose, most of his r. arm, maenad's r. forearm, inner surface of her leopard skin; *chiton* folds in maenad's lap have lost their glaze lines and bear groups of diagonal scratches. Side A: surface of second satyr worn; third satyr most affected, noticeably in r. arm, face, torso, and l. hand; surface scraped over face and upper body of maenad at r. Side B: damaged are r. arm of l. maenad, r. hand of satyr to her r., top of head of other maenad.

Preliminary sketch: numerous multiple lines, not always followed. A few areas sketched out in broad, generalized plan. Makron outlines whole bodies under drapery, completely marks out *thyrsoi*, dress folds, cloaks, and secondary objects, even though covered in final picture. Int.: Maenad—under drapery; inside jaw and nose; upper line of r. leg continued back under *chiton;* line of belt continued across r. thigh; leopard-skin dots marked with small incised circles; glaze, filling up this incision, gives raised quality to dots. Satyr—line of skin sketched across l. leg; upper r. arm contours deeply sketched. Side A: First satyr—numerous arcs 0.002-0.004 m. within buttocks; sketch of r. leg 0.002 m. to the left; front edge of leopard cloak marked over r. forearm and under r. leg; lines within contour of r. arm. Second figure—numerous verticals in neck of maenad; lines continuing r. foreleg and foot of first satyr, under her skirt (his heel visible only in glaze); drapery sketch lines across *thyrsos*. Third figure—lines within edges of back leg; numerous other lines within contours of stomach and thighs. Second maenad—body contours; inside face and l. leg. Third satyr—numerous lines within back leg; indication of *thyrsos,* eliminated in final figure; handle end at hip level. Rightmost maenad—*thyrsos* marked across body; inside r. arm. Goat—no lines. Side B: not available for study.

Glaze used throughout, except on interior of handles and between their attachment points. Narrow reserve bands define rim. Foot edge, its resting surface, and interior of foot stem also reserved. Relief contour throughout, except for hair contours, satyr tails, and goat fringe, which are reserved. Dilute glaze: for male, not female anatomy. Red: ivy wreaths, dotted vines, double fillets, and belts.

Provenance: Said to come from Athens. Charles L. Morley to Frederick M. Watkins; Bequest to the Fogg Art Museum, Harvard University, 1972.41.

Int.: *Satyr and maenad*
Ext.: *Battle of satyrs and maenads*

Satyrs and maenads were well loved by Makron. These aggressive satyrs and agile maenads interact in a love battle. Their bodies, set in postures of advance and retreat, are ornamented by billowing drapery and spotted skins. The *thyrsos*-swinging maenads momentarily hold the lusty followers of Dionysos at bay.

A goat, emblem of lechery, observes the woodland frolic; he is protected by a handle, as in the Robinson cup (*ARV,* 463, no. 51; *CVA,* Robinson 2 [USA 6], 259, pl. 16). The satyr crouched under the other handle is making a sneak rear attack on a maenad. He recalls the subhandle satyr attacking Hera on a cup by the Brygos Painter in London (British Museum E 65; *ARV,* 370, no. 13) and a reveller by the same painter, in Berlin (F 2309; *CVA,* Berlin 2 [Germany 21], pl. 69 [998], fig. 3; *ARV,* 373, no. 46).

The damaged couple in the interior probably should be restored with their right hands crossing in front of the maenad's spotted cloak. The pair on Side A of Munich 2654 (*ARV,* 462, no. 47; A. Furtwängler and K. Reichold, *Griechische Vasenmalerei,* Series 1-3 [Munich, 1904], 46) would look thus if bounded by a *tondo.* The couple on the Watkins cup concentrates on the dance, unlike two similar pairs by Makron; one, an amorous satyr seducing a leopard-swinging maenad inside a cup in the Louvre (G 144; *ARV,* 462, no. 43); the other, the fleeing maenad inside the Munich cup mentioned above, who jabs her *thyrsos* between the satyr's legs.

This attractive cup deserves further study of its lively gestures, variety in cloaks, excited anatomy, and fine faces. It falls within Makron's middle period, about 490-480 B.C.

AHA and KMP

Bibliography: Fogg, *Ancient Art,* 35, no. 275, pl. 82; *ARV,* 462, no. 45; A. H. Ashmead and K. M. Phillips, "An Unpublished Cup by Makron in Philadelphia," *AJA,* 70 (1966), pl. 91 (handle zones); *Paralipomena,* 377, no. 45.

22

Red-Figure Kylix (Type B)

Greek, Attic, painted by Onesimos, ca. 490-480 B.C.

H. to rim 3⅞ in. (0.099 m.); H. at handles 4 in. (0.101 m.);
Diam. of bowl 9⅜ in. (0.239 m.); W. with handles 12¼ in.
(0. 313 m.); Diam. of foot 3⅞ in. (0.098 m.); Diam. of
tondo 6⅛ in. (0.155 m.)

Once broken into 42 pieces, mended without repainting.
Major lacunae: interior–shield and maeander; Side A–
below armpit, in shield and greaves of first figure; minor
portions missing from trainer's robe. Glaze inside has
fired an iridescent charcoal. Grayish glaze discoloration
around first and second figures on Side A; glaze oxidized
red around arm of third figure. Ring of discoloration on
outside, just below knee level, is result of stacking in kiln
(see Noble, *Techniques*, 79-80). Glaze on underside of
foot fired gray; some partial bands of red showing
through. Lighter toned sections of athlete's body in *tondo*
are alterations due to salts.

Preliminary sketch lines are wide and single. Few changes
made from sketch, hence few lines are visible. Two frontal
shields on exterior are compass outlined; center points
visible. Interior: some lines within greaves and inside feet;
arcs within, echoing smaller arcs of *halteres,* may indicate
these were planned further apart. Side A: lines within
contours of first figure's r. arm; both legs of trainer
indicated under drapery; inside upper contours of third
figure's feet. Side B: just within contour of forward leg of
third figure.

Glaze used throughout, except on interior of handles and
between their attachment points, band within edge of rim,
edge of foot, its resting surface, and interior of stem.
Relief contour: Int.–throughout, except where upper
greave touches border, below toes, along helmet crest;
head contour reserved. Ext.–throughout, except crests;
knobby staff has reserved contour around handle, below
handle, in segment between hand and staff on l. side;
trainer's head contour reserved. Dilute glaze used extensively for muscles. The tiny circles indicating male nipples
are an especially fine touch. Thinned dark brown glaze
used for moustache, whiskers, and imperial of *tondo*
athlete. Red: Int.–fillet, *haltere* cords, inscription.
Side A–trainer's wreath, inscription, *haltere* cords.
Side B–inscription.

Provenance: Said to come from Greece. Private collection
of Joseph Brummer to Frederick M. Watkins, 1948;
Bequest to the Fogg Art Museum, Harvard University,
1972.39.

Int.: *Hoplitodromos*
Side A: *Trainer and two athletes*
Side B: *Three armed runners*

On the interior of the cup, an older nude athlete practices
his starts for the race in armor. He has laid aside his
shield, helmet, and greaves, seeming to have balanced
them against the edge of the *tondo*. The *halteres* (jumping
weights) hung in the background provide a purely athletic
note. The *hoplitodromos,* or armed runner, stoops, arm
extended, fingers spread, feet separated, the rear heel
slightly off the ground. A thin red fillet and a thicker wool
sash, looped in back, tie down his hair. He sports a long
imperial, moustache, and whiskers. The face is not handsome, yet it is full of character. The nose, in particular, is
strongly curved and large, with a pronounced nostril. The
lips are parted to draw in breath for a quick start. An
inscription ΗΟ ΠΑΙΣ (the sigma, damaged by a crack, is
incomplete), retrograde, runs from his hip to the Attic
helmet. Around the *tondo* lies a border of neatly drawn
interlocking meander pairs; the squeezed "fellow" at
eleven o'clock marks the terminus. The meander border
was traced within the confines of two thin bands.

The exterior develops the *hoplitodromos* theme. On
Side A a young *paidotribe* (trainer) instructs an athlete,
who is picking up his shield. The *paidotribe* wears a
voluminous mantle and a wreath; he rests his right arm
on a knobbed staff and points out correct technique with
a forked stick. The pupil, having already donned helmet
and greaves, bends over and grasps the *porpax* (central
metal arm band) with his left hand, preparatory to hoist-
ing the shield shoulder-high. A second athlete, already
armed, assumes the starting pose. His feet, firmly planted,
reverse the stance of the *tondo* figure. His free arm is
extended, the hand tilted up, palm down, fingers spread.
Behind him is a pick; *halteres* hang from the wall. ΗΟ ΠΑΙΣ
was inscribed between the first figure's shoulder and the
lower tip of the forked rod. ΚΑΛΟΣ (the sigma, now
nearly lost, was just above the pick) lies between the
trainer's cloak and the top of the pick.

The three armed runners of Side B are actively practicing. Two are running, unencumbered by their shields. The end men run toward the center; their poses are very similar—bodies bent forward, legs far apart, forward hand out with spread fingers. The central athlete moves forward yet leans back, a stance popular in early fifth-century art. He may be checking himself upon arrival at the start (Beazley, *BSA*, 8), or stopping to round the turning post, or halting at the finish line (E. N. Gardiner, "Notes on the Greek Foot Race," *JHS*, 23 [1903], 278-279, 289). A discus hangs in its sack; a shield lies on the ground to one side. HO ΠΑΙΣ is inscribed below the left arm of the first runner. The two shields on this side, the two on Side A, and the badly preserved shield on the interior were decorated with a six- or seven-lobed leaf. The identification of this leaf is unsure; fig, plane tree, horse chestnut, parsley, or lupine have been suggestions. The use of identical shield charges may be a touch of realism, implying that all belong to one gymnasium (F. Hauser, "Zur Tübinger Bronze II," *JdI*, 10 [1895], 199). The exterior pictures were edged above and below by reserved lines.

The *hoplitodromos* theme is preserved on one other cup by Onesimos, in the Schweizer Collection, Arlesheim (*ARV*, 323, no. 56), and on a cup fragment by him in the Cabinet des Médailles (inv. no. 666; *ARV*, 323, no. 57). The Arlesheim kylix, which displays somewhat richer drapery, hairier bodies, and a fine *podanipter* (basin), is strikingly close in composition and style; note the thin bodies, elongated legs, narrow eyes, and almost affected hand gestures. Perhaps these two cups were conceived as a pair—complements to each other, but not copies—for together they explore the movements of armed runners. The bearded *tondo* runner in the Schweizer cup is cousin to the youth sponging himself over a *podanipter,* inside a cup by Onesimos (Louvre, G 291; *ARV*, 322, no. 36), on the outside of which athletes draw water and apply strigils. This athletic theme is repeated on another Onesimos cup (Louvre, G 297; *ARV*, 322, no. 35).

The theme of an armed runner may have been chosen by a customer who was a *hoplitodromos.* The topic is pictured most frequently by two associates of Onesimos, the Antiphon and Colmar Painters. It is a subject most common about 500-480 B.C. and appears often on small cups, sometimes on other small vases, less often on large pots. As far as is known, the armed race motif does not antedate the beginning of red-figure, except on amphorae. (The earliest prize amphora is Museo Civico, Bologna, inv. no. 198; *CVA*, Bologna 2 [Italy 7], pl. 1 [344]; von Brauchitsch, *Die panathenäischen Preisamphoren* [Leipzig, 1910], 21, no. 17, dated 525-515 B.C.)

This cup is a good piece of about 490-480 B.C. The interior is finely composed and drawn. The exterior, although with some delicate touches in interior lines and variety to the moustaches, is more routine and less elaborate.

AHA and KMP

Bibliography: J. D. Beazley, "A Hoplitodromos Cup," *BSA*, 46 (1951), 10-11; *ARV*, 323, no. 55.

23

Red-Figure Lekythos

Greek, Attic, attributed to the Berlin Painter [Beazley], ca. 480 B.C.

H. 13⅜ in. (0.34 m.); Diam. 4½ in. (0.114 m.)

Broken and repaired. Small areas restored, including section of garment at knee level. Slight abrasion in center of chest. Preliminary sketch: legs and l. arm indicated under drapery. Margin of drapery behind figure was sketched to r. of actual glaze line. Dilute glaze: fine folds of *chiton.* Red: ivy leaves, wreath in hair.

Provenance: Said to come from Attica. Charles L. Morley to Frederick M. Watkins, 1942; Bequest to the Fogg Art Museum, Harvard University, 1972.44.

Dionysos with a kantharos

Dionysos, the god of wine, is identified by the bacchanalian ivy garland in his hair and the drinking cup, or kantharos, in his right hand. Kantharoi frequently occur on vase paintings as attributes of Dionysos, although actual pottery examples are rare. Their spindly shape, with attenuated curving handles, suggests that these cups were better suited to execution in metal.

The god carries a knotty staff and a branch of ivy in his left hand. He wears a thin linen *chiton* that falls into many narrow pleats, under a heavier *himation,* weighted at the corners so that it will drape attractively. The figure stands on an ivy border. On the neck of the vase is a band of egg-and-dart motif.

Attic vase painters, almost without exception, specialized in either cups or pots (i.e. all other shapes). The Berlin Painter, who worked between 500 and 460 B.C., and the Kleophrades Painter (see No. 20) are considered to be the pre-eminent pot-painters of the late archaic period. The Berlin Painter characteristically reduces his pictorial narrative to its barest essentials. Often, as here, a single figure adorns the vase. His emphasis is on a lively, expressive contour; a common device by which he enlivens his silhouettes is to incorporate long projecting objects, such as staffs, spears, or simply extended limbs. Here the spray of ivy repeats the line of the garland and the contour of the figure's left shoulder, while the staff echoes and accentuates the long fall of drapery over the forearm.

The vase belongs to the early – and best – phase of the artist's career.

SD

Bibliography: Fogg, Ancient Art, 35, no. 272, pl. 80; *ARV,* 211, no. 197.

24

Red-Figure Lekythos

Greek, Attic, attributed to the manner of Douris
[Beazley], ca. 480-470 B.C.

H. 11¹³⁄₁₆ in. (0.30 m.)

Intact. Dilute glaze used for folds on upper part of *chiton*. Traces of preliminary sketch can be seen at shoulder.

Provenance: Said to come from Gela, possibly with No. 27. Sale, Paris, Hôtel Drouot, June 17-19, 1912; Jacob Hirsch to Frederick M. Watkins, 1941; Gift to the Fogg Art Museum, Harvard University, 1959.193.

Woman holding alabastron

A woman dressed in *chiton, himation,* and *sakkos* looks to the right. In her outstretched hand she holds an alabastron. Behind her is a small chest. On the neck are tongues; at the base, two stopped meanders, a cross-square, then four stopped meanders.

The shape and decoration of this lekythos relate it to Douris's late period. Compare lekythoi in Vienna (Univ. 526 a; *ARV*, 447, no. 272) and in Boston (inv. no. 95.41; *ARV*, 447, no. 270). All three are characterized by sparse decoration on the neck, no decoration on the shoulder, and the rather careless meander ground line.

DB

Bibliography: Hôtel Drouot, *Collection de feu M. Jean P. Lambros* [Athens] *et de M. Giovanni Dattari* [Cairo] (Paris, June 17-19, 1912), pl. 7, no. 51; Hôtel Drouot, *Collection Hirsch* (Paris, June 30-July 2, 1921), pl. 3, no. 169; *ARV,* 451, no. 34; Buitron, *Attic Vases,* 108, no. 58.

25

Red-Figure Nolan Amphora

Greek, Attic, attributed to the Providence Painter [D. von Bothmer], 485-475 B.C.

H. 12⅜ in. (0.318 m.); W. at mouth 5⁹⁄₁₆ in. (0.142 m.); W. at handles 6⁵⁄₁₆ in. (0.179 m.); W. at base 3⁷⁄₁₆ in. (0.088 m.)

Intact. Slight flaking on surface. Small crack in r. handle. Base attached separately. Preliminary sketch: Side A– arms and legs of man and woman, folds of *himations*, hem of woman's *chiton;* Side B–legs and feet of man, folds and hem of *himation*. Relief contour throughout. Dilute glaze: Side A–folds of woman's *himation* and cap, edges of hair and beard of man; Side B–edges of hair and beard of man. Red: Side A–letters, wreath held by woman, wreath on man's head.

Provenance: Jacob Hirsch to Frederick M. Watkins, 1950; Bequest to the Fogg Art Museum, Harvard University, 1972.45.

Side A: *Woman and man exchanging a wreath*
Side B: *Man with a staff*

A border of double palmettes and curving tendrils encircles the body of the vase, and a palmette with tendrils lies beneath each handle. On Side A a woman is seated on a straight-backed chair. She offers a garland or wreath to a man who stands before her, leaning heavily upon a rough-hewn staff. The woman is dressed in a *himation* over a finely-pleated *chiton*. The folds of the garment fall loosely and gracefully about the supple curves of her body. A brimmed cap, faintly decorated with tiny dots, rests upon her curls, which are clearly defined by clusters of small black dots. A round earring is her only ornament. The lady sits proud and erect, carefully concentrating on offering the wreath.

The man is dressed in a floor-length *himation;* its abundant folds are drawn loosely about his body, directly beneath his breast, and held in place by the left forearm at the elbow. His hair is a neat little black cap, shadowed with tufts of red at the nape of the neck and at the edge of the forehead. There is a faint trace of a garland resting on the crown of his head. The whiskers of his full beard are emphasized by tiny red and black striations. His eye is wide and alert, and he smiles with satisfaction. Between the two figures stands a wide-mouthed basket, decorated with a tiny scalloped design enclosed by two thin parallel

bands at the upper part of the foot. It has been overpainted, possibly due to an earlier abrasion. It may represent the lady's work basket *(kalathos)*, filled with skeins of unspun wool. Many Greek vases depict *hetairai*, or courtesans, engaged in spinning and weaving; an Attic white-ground lekythos by the Pan Painter of ca. 470 B.C., in the Norbert Schimmel Collection, shows a lady standing beside a wool basket of a design similar to that on the Watkins amphora.

Between the heads of the man and woman an inscription, KALE ("beautiful one") can be read. There is also an inscription beneath the extended right arm of the man, but part of it has been worn away and the exact meaning is unclear. It has, however, been interpreted as ΚΑΛΟΣ ("handsome one"). The Schimmel lekythos cited above bears a similar inscription.

Side B shows a bearded man in profile. Both feet are firmly planted on the ground, his right shoulder is bare, and his right arm extends holding a long staff. His massive body is hidden beneath a thick floor-length cloak with few heavy folds, weighted at the bottom so as to hang evenly. His black hair is punctuated by small patches of light red; the whiskers of his full beard are finely noted by tiny pin-like strokes. There is a striking similarity between his features and those of the man on the other side of the amphora. Are they brothers or cousins, or possibly two depictions of the same character? His attitude is serious and pensive; his pose suggests that he is waiting for something. Interpretations of the scenes must, however, remain speculative.

Despite its simple composition, the painting is rich in details. Such features as the woman's hair, the men's whiskers, and their toes and fingers are carefully executed. A sense of excitement permeates the characters; a generally happy mood has been created. The style of the Providence Painter is derived from that of the Berlin Painter, but, as Beazley has said, it is a style which is not poetry, but "sober, honest, often noble prose with a masculine beauty of its own" (*ARVAM*, 76).

JWB

Bibliography: J. D. Beazley, *Attic Red-Figure Vases in American Museums* (Cambridge, 1918), 76; Fogg, *Ancient Art*, 35, no. 277, pls. 82, 84; *ARV*, 638, no. 43.

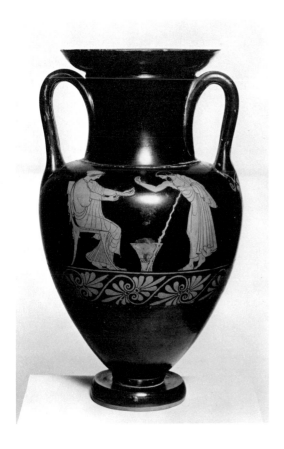

26

Red-Figure Pelike

Greek, Attic, attributed to the manner of the Pig Painter [Beazley], ca. 470-450 B.C.

H. 14¾ in. (0.375 m.)

Broken and repaired; missing pieces restored and painted. Dilute glaze used for edge of woman's hair, edge of man's beard, inner markings on one youth. Red: ivy wreaths, fillet on woman's *sakkos,* cords tied to lyres and cithara, ends of strings at pegs of crossbar.

Provenance: Frederick M. Watkins; Gift to the Fogg Art Museum, Harvard University, 1959.188.

Side A: *Komos*
Side B: *Komos*

On Side A a woman with a *sakkos* on her head plays a small cithara; her mouth is open and her head back, indicating that she is singing. On the left is a youth with a walking stick and a *barbiton* (long-armed lyre); on the right a youth lifts a column-krater decorated with a garland of ivy. Between the last youth and the woman is a *diphros* (small stool) on which drapery is folded.

Side B shows two youths and a man walking to the right. The first youth, carrying a wineskin and an oinochoe, turns back toward his companions. The second youth plays a flute; the man carries a pointed amphora and a lyre. All three wear ivy wreaths in their hair and *chlamides* over their shoulders.

Above the figures on both sides are lotus buds with dots in the interstices; circling the vase below is a simple rightward key between double lines.

The Pig Painter is a close follower of Myson and an able mannerist of the early free period. He is named for the two pigs on a pelike in Cambridge (inv. no. 9.17; *ARV,* 564, no. 27) showing Odysseus and Eumaios. He was fond of large vases, especially column-kraters and pelikai, as was the mannerist school in general. Characteristic of his style are the small eyes, thin moustache, and stylized ears. He is distinguished for his rhythmical compositions, which are especially noteworthy on Side B of this vase.

DB

Bibliography: ARV, 566, no. 8; Buitron, *Attic Vases,* 112, no. 61.

27

Red-Figure Hydria (Kalpis)

Greek, Attic, attributed to the Villa Giulia Painter
[Beazley], ca. 460-450 B.C.

H. 10⅞ in. (0.277 m.)

Intact; some abrasion of glaze. Dilute glaze used for
anatomical markings, lines on drapery. Red: fillet of youth
and of woman on l.

Provenance: Said to come from Gela. Jacob Hirsch to
Frederick M. Watkins, 1941; Bequest to the Fogg Art
Museum, Harvard University, 1972.46.

Youth between two women

A nude youth with his cloak over his left shoulder and a
stick in one hand stands in the center. On the left a woman
runs off, looking back; on the right is a woman with one
hand raised. Above and below are triple meanders
alternating with cross-squares; on the lip is an egg-and-
dot pattern.

   The Villa Giulia Painter stands in the tradition of
Douris and, like him, prefers subdued and refined figures
depicted with a polished technique. His harmonious
compositions are in opposition to the ambitious efforts of
his contemporary, the Niobid Painter. Fond of scenes of
everyday life, he employs certain stock types such as the
women and youth on this vase. Although the figures
appear serene, the air is tense. The subject, however,
remains unexplained. The vase is said to be from Gela
but may be the vase described by E. Peterson in "Funde,"
RM, 8 (1893), 340, no. 26; if so, it is probably from
Curti or Capua (*ARV,* 623, no. 62).

DB

Bibliography: ARV, 623, no. 62; Buitron, *Attic Vases,*
120, no. 66.

70

28

White-Ground Lekythos

Greek, Attic, attributed to the Achilles Painter [Beazley], ca. 450-440 B.C.

H. 13½ in. (0.34 m.); Diam. 4 in. (0.102 m.)

Intact; some abrasion of surface; slight dent in side between the figures. Preliminary sketch: general outlines of bodies beneath drapery and of garments. Where red pigment remains, it does not follow sketch lines exactly. Dilute glaze: drawing and hair. Matte red iron-oxide pigment on garment of r. figure. Color probably used on garment of l. figure has worn off. Significant fading has occurred since publication of vase in 1954.

Provenance: Frederick M. Watkins; Bequest to the Fogg Art Museum, Harvard University, 1972.43.

Mistress and maid

Lekythoi were commonly used as oil containers. However, those decorated in the white-ground technique were often filled with perfumed olive oil and dedicated as grave gifts, possibly because the instability of their fragile surface would not permit daily use. From about the middle of the fifth century on, their decoration often alludes to their funerary association. Here the artist depicts a woman, at right, and her maid, who carries a large basket, perhaps filled with gifts for the grave. Their mien is solemn, but it conveys a sense of spiritual strength that is characteristic of the best work of the Achilles Painter. A hand mirror hangs on the wall to the right of the mistress's head, setting the scene in an interior and perhaps alluding to the beauty of the deceased. Above the figures is a band of alternating leftward and rightward triple meanders, alternating with saltires; on the shoulder of the vase, palmettes and volutes; at the neck, an egg pattern. Beazley relates the piece to two similar lekythoi in Athens (*ARV*, 999-1000, cf. nos. 184-185).

The drawing is executed over the fine white-slip ground in dilute glaze that fires with a shiny surface, varying in color from a rich golden brown to an almost transparent neutral. The artist has first sketched out the nude figures, then drawn clothing around them, preparatory to filling in the garments with brilliant color that would mask the underdrawing. Because the dilute outline glaze was more durable than the colored pigment, the artist's "preliminary sketch" is once again revealed. A puzzling feature is that in a few places (the mistress's nose, her hem at the right ankle, and the maid's garment outline behind the right thigh) the glaze line or color seems to continue through an abraded area.

The Achilles Painter was a pupil of the Berlin Painter (see No. 23). There has been speculation that he may even have been the son of the older painter, since among the fifth-century Greeks trades were often passed on from generation to generation within a family. He became the principal master of white-ground lekythoi in the third quarter of the century, establishing a system of decorating these vases with a few solemn, standing or seated figures that was widely adopted by his many followers and imitators. Working at the time that the Parthenon frieze was being executed in Athens, he imbues his figures with a measure of the dignity and grace that epitomize classical Greek art.

With an eye to economy—perhaps enforced by law (see Noble, *Techniques*, 24)—many lekythoi intended for graves were constructed with a small inner cup attached to the lower part of the neck. Thus, they could appear to be full when containing only a few ounces of oil. This vessel has such a false bottom; the small hole in the black zone beneath the woman at the right is the vent hole, through which gases could escape from the sealed lower chamber during firing.

SD

Bibliography: Fogg, *Ancient Art,* 37, no. 297, pl. 88; *ARV,* 1000, no. 186.

29

Red-Figure Nolan Amphora

Greek, Attic, attributed to a painter in the Group of Polygnotos [Beazley], ca. 450-440 B.C.

H. 14⅜ in. (0.365 m.); Diam. 6½ in. (0.167 m.)

Broken and repaired. Handles filed down at lower ends, probably during earlier inaccurate restoration. Heavy overpaint removed and vase correctly reassembled by Fogg Conservation Laboratory, 1972. (Photographs are before restoration.) Incised on foot: AIKA. Preliminary sketch lines indicate bodies beneath drapery; especially visible in legs of Pluton, Demeter. Background glaze clumsily applied, running over ends of meander bands and over contours of figures in some places. Red: stalks and linear detailing of wheat heads, strings of *petasos*.

Provenance: V. Simkhovitch; Charles L. Morley to Frederick M. Watkins; Gift to the Fogg Art Museum, Harvard University, 1959.187.

Side A: *Demeter and Triptolemos*
Side B: *Pluton*

The figures on both sides of the vase are associated with the myth of Persephone's abduction to the underworld. On Side A Demeter offers three stalks of wheat to Triptolemos; on Side B Pluton is shown as god of wealth and hence fertility. The figures stand on bands of double leftward meanders alternating with saltires.

When Demeter, goddess of grain, learned that her daughter Persephone had been seized by Pluton (or Hades), god of the underworld, she caused the earth to become desolate and crops to wither and die. Only after an agreement had been made that Persephone would spend part of each year with her mother and part in the under-world did Demeter revoke her curse on the land, sending Triptolemos, son of a couple who had befriended her during her grief, as her emissary to carry both seed and the art of planting it far and wide. The Eleusinian Mysteries—secret rites performed at Eleusis—re-enacted this myth, which allegorically explains the changing of the seasons, the alternation of fertility and barrenness in the fields.

Here Pluton, wrapped in a *himation,* is identified as god of wealth by the cornucopia he carries. In his right hand is a lotus-tipped staff. Demeter holds a similar staff in her left hand as she passes the wheat to Triptolemos, who

is appropriately attired for travelling in a short cloak *(chlamys)* and broad-brimmed hat *(petasos)*. He holds two spears.

The looser drawing style and more fluid arrangement of drapery folds here are characteristic of the "free style" of vase painting that evolved after mid-century and was practiced by Polygnotos and his prolific school. During this period of Periclean patronage of the "major" arts—architecture, painting, and sculpture—vase-painting no longer attracted the leading artistic talents as it had earlier. The execution of this vase is hasty; contours are imprecise, and areas such as Demeter's right foot are crudely rendered. Nevertheless, the artist is aware of major advances in sculpture and large-scale painting, in which the body was being treated as an integral whole, a rounded form existing in a three-dimensional space. The figures on this vase exist more convincingly in a shallow spatial plane parallel to the vase's surface. Three-quarter views and foreshortening are successfully under-taken. Garments no longer consist of an arbitrary pattern of folds imposed over the body; their draping is irregular, reflecting the play of underlying forms. The figures have an easy, relaxed stance not unrelated to the *contrapposto* of statues by Phidias. However, the vase-painter's idiom does not readily lend itself to expressing sculptural plasticity and gradual spatial transitions, and the result is less than satisfactory.

SD

Bibliography: ARV, 1059, no. 6. On representations of Demeter and Triptolemos, see K. Friis-Johansen, "Triptolemos og Theseus," *Meddelelser fra Ny Carlsberg Glyptothek,* 26 (1969), 15-40.

74

30

Squat Lekythos

Greek, South Italian, Apulian, probably by the Darios Painter, ca. 330-300 B.C.

H. 7 in. (0.179 m.); Diam. 3⁵⁄₁₆ in. (0.084 m.)

Mended, with some minor restorations. Added white and yellow paint. Incision defines tongues on body above base.

Provenance: A. Emmerich Gallery to Frederick M. Watkins, 1968; Bequest to the Fogg Art Museum, Harvard University, 1972.325.

The squat lekythos, a form of oil container favored in Athens during the late fifth and first half of the fourth centuries B.C., was absorbed into the repertoire of painted vases made in the Apulian region of southeastern Italy during the late fourth century. The Watkins example has a ring foot with three ridges. A necklace of tongue patterns encircles the shoulder; vertical stripes adorn the neck. The main decorative motif on the vase is elegantly adapted to its shape: a youthful head, wearing the eastern Phrygian cap and looking to the left, emerges from the calyx of a trumpet-shaped flower. Substantial branches, sprouting smaller blossoms and coiled tendrils, curl upward on either side of the central motif. An elaborate palmette of 21 petals, done in traditional red-figure technique, dominates the zone under the handle. The cap and the edge of the blossom are rendered in added yellow. Beneath the cap, delicate wavy strokes in dilute glaze define trailing locks of hair.

The motif of a head rising from a flower is not uncommon in Apulian vase painting; in Roman art, it is a frequent adjunct to portraits, often posthumous ones (see H. Jucker, *Das Bildnis im Blätterkelch* [Olten, 1961]). The identity of the head on the Watkins lekythos is uncertain. While it is reminiscent of heads in similar eastern headdresses that appear on Attic red-figure squat lekythoi of the later fifth century B.C. (e.g. *Hesperia Art Bulletin*, 33, no. A6), the head is more likely that of Attis, the youth who was the beloved of Cybele.

The Darios Painter was fond of characters and costumes derived from sources in the Near East. His most famous work, for which he is named, is the monumental volute krater in the Naples Museum depicting the court of Darios I (552-486 B.C.), the Achaemenian Persian king who launched the expedition against Marathon and who appears in the *Persians* of Aeschylus. The Darios Painter is known to have done other squat lekythoi. Might this vase be a small companion to a large funerary vase or group of vases intended for an individual tomb, some if not all decorated with mythical subjects of Near Eastern inspiration (cf. A. Oliver, Jr., "The Reconstruction of Two Apulian Tomb Groups," *AntK*, Beiheft 5 [Bern, 1968]; also Antikenmuseum Basel, *Neuerwerbungen und Leihgabenwechsel*, 3 [1971], 23-24, nos. 190-197).

DGM

Bibliography: A. Emmerich Gallery, *Art of the Ancients* (New York, 1968), 37, no. 45. On the Darios Painter, see M. Schmidt, *Der Dareiosmaler und seine Umkreis* (Münster, 1960); A. Stenico, "Pittore di Dario," *EAA*, 3 (1960), 10-12.

31

Bearded Male Head from a Grave Relief

Greek, Attic, 400-380 B.C.

Marble, H. 8 in. (0.203 m.); W. 5¾ in. (0.15 m.)

Forehead chipped; nose partially broken and chipped at bridge; lower r. half of beard to center of chin chipped and worn. Under ultraviolet light a bright orange fluorescence occurs over approximately half of r. side of face. Comparative spectrographic analysis of samples from various locations on surface of marble has revealed a lead compound in areas that fluoresce orange; little or no lead has been found in other areas. These findings were confirmed by microchemical analysis.

Provenance: Charles L. Morley to Frederick M. Watkins, 1949; Bequest to the Fogg Art Museum, Harvard University, 1972.50.

This finely executed marble head of a youth is an excellent example of the vital, impressionistic elements that characterized the Attic spirit. The man's jaw is firmly set, his mouth closed, his lips thick and well-defined. His nose, chipped from the bridge to the middle, is large and full. His wide and deeply set eyes intensify his expression; the left eye is set slightly lower than the right. The brow is faintly furrowed, the cheekbones are high and clearly delineated, and a fine, rich patina gives his complexion a warm glow. The short beard framing his cheeks and chin is indicated by a rough uneven texture, accented with little clumps of sparse relief. The short locks of hair adhere firmly to the head in a close-fitting cap; the waves and curls are defined by rich light and shadow effects.

His face slightly turned to the right in a three-quarter view, the youth gazes out at the spectator with a serious and thoughtful attitude. The initial impression of cool arrogance is tempered by a slight hint of pathos and self-contained sadness. This sentimental expression thus reflects with eloquence and refinement the individual personality of this meditating young man. Modeled with a soft and masterful touch, this head possesses a tremendous sense of strength and solidity. Tension, vitality, and energy can be read in the eyes, mouth and brow.

Becatti feels that this marble head of a youth probably comes from a grave relief because of its irregular "sliced-off" posterior plane, but that it recalls the style of the Parthenon period. He points out that the structure of the eyes and mouth, as well as the decorative modeling of the hair and forehead, can be convincingly compared with a number of heads of figures from the Parthenon frieze. While the Watkins head is especially close in its high relief style to such heads as those of Zeus, the priests, or the magistrates from the east frieze of the Parthenon, its slightly larger dimensions make it unlikely that it was at one time actually a part of the Parthenon frieze. Becatti suggests that it is quite possible that the sculptor of the Watkins head of a youth might have also contributed to the execution of the Panathenaic procession on the Parthenon.

JWB

Bibliography: G. Becatti, *Problemi Fidiaci* (Milan, 1951), 13-15, pl. 2: 2-3; Fogg, *Ancient Art,* 27, no. 147, pl. 37.

Handle and Top of a Spouted Jug

Etruscan or Campanian, early 5th century B.C.

Bronze. Handle: L. 7 in. (0.178 m.); spout: L. 4½ in.
(0.114 m.), W. 2⅞ in. (0.072 m.); head at top of handle:
H. 1⅛ in. (0.027 m.), W. ⅝ in. (0.017 m.); head at bottom
of handle: H. 1⅝ in. (0.041 m.), W. 1¼ in. (0.032 m.)

Handle solid cast, joined to mouth of vessel by casting
on. Very smooth turquoise patina, perhaps indicating tin
enrichment of surface. Elaborate cold-working after
casting; chatter-marks of chisel-like tracer tool visible in
guilloche pattern; dots drilled. Mouth of vessel appears
to have been annealed after casting and crimped on either
side of handle; cracks in the two rear lobes of mouth
have resulted from this process.

Provenance: Frederick M. Watkins; Bequest to the Fogg
Art Museum, Harvard University, 1972.51.

The body of this jug has been destroyed, but it was
probably of the form shown in the drawing here. Its use
in pouring wine is appropriately supervised by a bearded
satyr at the upper end of the handle, who looks into the
mouth of the vessel. A second satyr's head decorates the
opposite end of the fluted handle.

The vessel's mouth and neck are richly decorated.
The lip has a row of beading inside an egg-and-dart
molding. Around the mouth run several fillet and bead
moldings and a broad band of guilloche punctuated by
dots. The neck is broken off evenly at the upper margin
of a second band of similar decoration; a fragment of the
second ornamental zone remains on one side.

Both its meticulous, ornate decoration and its unusually
smooth, light patina unite this vessel with a group in
New York (Richter, *Bronzes,* 180, esp. nos. 492, 547; no.
579, in silver with bronze handle) and a jar in Boston
(BMFA, *Bronzes,* 381, no. 527). The vessels at the Metropolitan Museum, with the exception of no. 492, were
reputedly found together in a tomb at Città Castellana,
site of the ancient Etruscan city, Falerii. The Boston bronze
also comes from Città Castellana. All combine the
distinctive guilloche-and-dot pattern with delicate bead,
fillet, and ovolo moldings.

Also in the tomb find were a jug of the same shape as
the Fogg example, with plain body and fluted handle, and
another jug similar in form but with trefoil mouth
(Richter, *Bronzes,* nos. 494, 493). Two vessels from the

tomb find—a jug and a *patera* (nos. 489 and 580)—have
handles decorated with satyrs whose heads are related
to those on the Watkins handle.

These correspondences suggest that the Watkins bronze
may have been made in the same workshop as the Città
Castellana group, or at least in the same vicinity and
at the same time. The resemblance of their patinas may
indicate that the metal of all the bronzes has a similar
composition, or that they were all buried under the same
conditions, or both.

Although the findspot of most of these bronzes is
known, their place of manufacture remains a matter for
speculation. Richter has hypothesized that the tomb group
was of Greek authorship because of its elegance of form
and the precision and delicacy of its workmanship. She
designates the two plainer pitchers, closest in shape to the
Watkins example, as Greek or Etruscan. V. Poulsen (Fogg,
Ancient Art) has suggested that the Watkins bronze
might be Campanian, an allegation that is strengthened
by the resemblance of the satyr heads to types of bearded
heads known among Campanian terra cottas. Vermeule
has classified the Boston jar as Etruscan. During the fifth
and most of the fourth century B.C., the greater part of
Campania, which had been settled by the Greeks, fell
under Etruscan rule. The art of this region reflects a min-
gling of Greek and Etruscan characteristics. The Watkins
jug, which also shows Greek and Etruscan traits in
combination, may be the product of such an area
of cultural overlap.

Vases of the shape of the Watkins piece, both Greek
and Etruscan, begin to appear in clay and metal in the late
sixth century (see Richter, *Bronzes,* no. 493); numerous
examples found in Etruscan tombs as late as the third
century testify to the popularity of the form in Etruria.
(A late example, with guilloche, is in the E. de Kolb
Collection; Fogg, *Master Bronzes,* 221, no. 224, ill.).

Jacobsthal has acknowledged the relationship between
vessels of this shape and the well-defined series of jugs of
the *Schnabelkanne* type; he suggests that the two groups
may have been produced in workshops near each other.
In trying to reconcile the discrepancy between the
excellent casting and sense of form of the *Schnabelkannen*
and their comparatively clumsy incised decoration, he
localizes the workshop in a provincial outpost in Umbria
or Picenum that had close ties with Vulci, a major
Etruscan bronze-working center. M. Guarducci and
F. Magi, however, feel that the *Schnabelkannen* were

made in Vulci itself. The careful incised detail and extensive use of bead and ovolo moldings also suggest connections between the Cività Castellana bronzes and a series of vessels decorated with tongue motif, discussed by K. A. Neugebauer, who localizes their workshop in the vicinity of Tarentum ("Reifarchaische Bronzevasen mit Zungenmuster," *RM,* 38-39 [1923-24], 341-440).

SD

Bibliography: Fogg, *Ancient Art,* 32, no. 230, pl. 71. On the patinas of bronzes with high tin content, see R. J. Gettens, "Patina: Noble and Vile," in *Art and Technology,* 60, 69. On casting-on, see A. Steinberg, "Techniques of Working Bronze," in Fogg, *Master Bronzes,* 12. For related satyr types, see P. J. Riis, "Some Campanian Types of Heads," *From the Collections of the Ny Carlsberg Glyptothek,* 2 (1938), 140-168. On the relationship with *Schnabelkannen,* see P. Jacobsthal and A. Langsdorff, *Die Bronzeschnabelkannen* (Berlin, 1929), 52. Other theories on the location of the *Schnabelkanne* workshop: F. Magi, *La Raccolta Benedetto Guglielmi nel Museo Vatincano Etrusco,* II (Vatican, 1941), 192-193, with bibl. for Guarducci and others. For a recent list of bronze jugs of the shape of the Fogg piece, S. Boucher, *Bronzes . . . des Musées de Lyon* (Lyon, 1970), 137, under nos. 147-148. A rather close parallel to the Watkins handle is S. Boucher, *Vienne, Bronzes antiques* (Paris, 1971), 139, no. 256, ill. pp. 139, 141.

33

Lasa or Nereid

Etruscan, late 4th century B.C.

Bronze, H. 8¼ in. (0.21 m.)

Solid cast. Dull green-black patina, with some red-brown areas on r. thigh and back. Object on head is hollow and open at top. Several small casting flaws on inside of r. ankle. Some mechanical cleaning undertaken in 1967.

Provenance: Charles L. Morley to Frederick M. Watkins, 1966; Gift to the Fogg Art Museum, Harvard University, 1966.109.

This statuette depicts a lightly-draped female figure with a sea monster coiled at her feet. She wears soft slippers, earrings, and a heavy bracelet above each elbow (the one on the right arm has several globular pendants or *bullae*). The sea monster has a dog-like head and serpentine tail, pointed beard, long crenate mid-dorsal fin, small dorsal fin, and two pectoral swimming fins.

The bronze resembles closely a winged figure from Perugia in the Museo Archeologico, Florence (Giglioli, *AE,* pl. 310:4), which supports a many-tiered inverted conical structure on its head and probably served as an incense burner. The unusual headgear of the Fogg bronze may be the base of a similar support. Like the Fogg piece, the Perugia figure holds an ointment flask (alabastron) in her left hand. She holds a smaller vessel, an aryballos, in her right. The Fogg figure's hand seems too tightly clenched to have held an aryballos. H. Hoffmann has suggested verbally that she may have grasped a dip-stick for extracting the contents of the alabastron.

Contemporary understanding of Etruscan mythology and religion is fragmentary, so it is difficult to identify the figure represented. Despite the absence of wings, H. Jucker and H. Hoffmann verbally see her as a Lasa—a generic name for the minor female genii that permeate Etruscan religion. Hoffmann feels that the alabastron relates to anointing the dead, emphasizing the Lasa's association with funerary rites. Jucker, however, stresses the Lasa's role as attendant of Turan, the Etruscan Aphrodite—the sea monster alludes to Aphrodite's birth from the sea, and the perfume vessel to her beauty. E. Langlotz verbally suggests that the bronze represents a nereid, or sea-nymph.

Nude or nearly nude female figures are not unusual in Etruscan art of this period. The stocky, athletic proportions of the Fogg bronze, the rather coarsely rendered, upswept hairdo, and the facial features–heart-shaped face, large almond eyes, and straight mouth–differ from those of the Perugia bronze. They find counterparts, however, among handle figures on Etruscan toilet-boxes (*cistae*) made in Praeneste in the fourth and third centuries B.C. Larger in scale than these handle figures, the Fogg bronze shows more refinement in detail than many of them, but the resemblance is strong enough to suggest that it may have been produced in a Praenestine workshop.

SD

Bibliography: Teitz, *Etruscan,* 90-91, no. 81, ill. p. 176; Fogg, *Master Bronzes,* 180, no. 184, ill. For a related Praenestine cista handle, see British Museum Br. 638; S. Haynes, *Etruscan Bronze Utensils* (London, 1965), pl. 13. On *ketoi* see K. Shepard, *The Fish-Tailed Monster in Greek and Etruscan Art* (New York, 1940).

34

Ledge Handle

Roman, late Republican or early Imperial (1st century B.C.) copy of a Greek prototype of ca. 500-450 B.C.

Bronze, H. 1¼ in. (0.033 m.); W. 3¾ in. (0.097 m.); D. 2¹⁄₁₆ in. (0.052 m.); Thickness at top rear ⅜ in. (0.01 m.)

Solid cast. Dark brown to black surface; calcium carbonate adhering in spots. Rams' eyes inlaid in silver, with punched pupils and outlined eyeballs. Hollow under-surface left rough.

Provenance: Frederick M. Watkins; Bequest to the Fogg Art Museum, Harvard University, 1972.53.

This massive handle, originally one of a pair, features a convex upper surface decorated with a linear palmette motif in low relief. Rams' heads in profile adorn the vertical sides of the handle.

The main palmette has a central blade-like petal flanked by two inward-curling tendrils, then by a pair of smaller, outward-curving petals. The calyx rests between the curls of two tangent tendrils that rise toward the rear corners of the handle. These terminate in hanging half-palmettes exactly like the central palmette in order and form of petals. The sides and rear of this panel are framed in a border of tiny beads. The vertical, slightly convex front edge of the handle, below the palmette panel, has a molding of elongated tongues or beads.

On the rams' heads, which correspond exactly to the handle's profile, punctate dots indicate the fleece. Carefully worked upturned ears project from within the curling rams' horns. Small incisions within the ear of the ram on the left represent fine strands of hair.

The concave back surface of the handle was attached–probably with solder–to a large vessel. The form of the ledge handle suggests that it was made for use on a large bell-krater, although no such vases in bronze are known to have survived. Compare the handles on pottery bell-kraters of the early fifth century B.C., such as the name-piece of the Pan Painter, in the Museum of Fine Arts, Boston (inv. no. 10.185; G. Chase and C. C. Vermeule, *Greek, Etruscan and Roman Art* [Boston, 1963], 110, no. 90).

A close parallel to the Watkins bronze, differing but slightly in size and detailing, is in the Thorvaldsens Museum, Copenhagen (unpublished). The ornament betrays a conscious attempt by the bronze-caster to imitate the Ionianizing decorative style of the early fifth century B.C. often seen in works from Greek centers in southern Italy. In form and function, the rams' heads are very like the ram's head terminals for handles of *paterae,* saucer-like vessels for pouring libations (cf. Fogg Art Museum, 1947.76; G.M.A. Hanfmann, "Acquisitions of the Fogg Art Museum: Sculpture and Figurines," *AJA,* 58 [1954], 227, pl. 38, fig. 11). *Patera* handles ending in animal heads are generally thought to be Hellenistic at the earliest. It is conceivable that the vessel to which this bronze handle belonged may have formed the centerpiece for an ensemble of ritual vessels with similar floral and animal ornament.

DGM

Bibliography: Unpublished.

35

Furniture Ornament with Bearded Head

Roman, 1st-2nd centuries A.D.

Bronze, H. 2¹⁵⁄₁₆ in. (0.075 m.); W. 1¹³⁄₁₆ in. (0.045 m.); D. 3¹⁵⁄₁₆ in. (0.099 m.)

Hollow cast. Dark green-black patina. Open under beard and head; rectangular socket behind head open at end; most of top missing. Modern stand shown in photograph.

Provenance: J. Carlebach Gallery, N.Y., to Frederick M. Watkins; Bequest to the Fogg Art Museum, Harvard University, 1972.54.

This bronze shows little evidence of cold-working after casting, indicating that it was intended for some utilitarian purpose that did not require careful finishing. The rectangular socket behind the head was made to slip over something–possibly the end of the wooden arm-rail of a formal chair or "throne." Greek thrones pictured on vases and reliefs often show animal heads capping the arm-rails (cf. Richter, *Furniture,* figs. 49, 50, 72, 73, 110). The Romans imitated many Greek furniture styles, often making some modifications; their taste leaned toward ornate decoration and combinations of various materials, such as metal and wood (Richter, *Furniture,* 97-98).

The bearded head itself also harks back to Greek models. Characteristics such as the modeling of the head, the treatment of the eyes with rounded indentations to indicate the irises, and the naturalistic, plastic curls which escape from the soft cap (*sakkos*) at the temples, make it clear that the head was produced no earlier than the late Hellenistic or Roman period. Nevertheless, the artist has attempted, by stylizing the beard and moustache, to capture the "antique" look of archaic Greek sculpture. Such archaizing constituted an important current in the art of this period, which admired and wished to emulate the values of earlier Greek civilization. The corkscrew curls of the beard, arranged neatly in two radiating rows, the convention of a small triangular beard under the lower lip (cf. No. 13), and the artificially regular, vigorously projecting arc formed by ears and beard, particularly telling in profile view, are archaistic features; some imitate traits of works of the archaic period, while others look to classical prototypes.

For other archaistic bearded heads, compare the herms from the Athenian Agora (E. B. Harrison, *Archaic and Archaistic Sculpture, The Athenian Agora*, 11 [Princeton, 1965], 108-176, pl. 40-57, esp. figs. 176, 182, 189). Eclectic archaizing is also evident in the relationship of the striking Jupiter statuette from Brée to the fifth-century Greek Zeus in Florence (see Fogg, *Master Bronzes*, 264, no. 255, with bibl.).

SD

Bibliography: Unpublished. On the archaistic style, see C. M. Havelock, "Archaistic Reliefs of the Hellenistic Period," *AJA*, 68 (1964), 43-58; idem, "Archaic as Survival Versus Archaistic as New Style," *AJA*, 69 (1965), 331-340, with bibl.

36

Repoussé Relief: Rider

Roman (probably early 2nd century A.D.) copy of a
Greek prototype of the 4th century B.C.

Bronze, H. 3⅞ in. (0.099 m.); W. 3⅛ in. (0.08 m.);
D. ¹¹⁄₁₆ in. (0.018 m.)

Repoussé with incised details. Dark surface; metallic in
color where rubbed (outer surface of thigh, knee, folds
of cloak). Missing: hind legs and l. front leg of horse;
tip of rider's foot. Edges of break in tip of r. foot are bent
upward. Holes worn in rider's knee and between knee
and horse's body. Channels for inlay on outer edge of
cloak and on horse's head for bridle. Silver inlaid fillet in
rider's hair, knob on his head. Perforations: upper edge
of cloak, l. side of relief; r. nipple; between mane and
rider's body at breast and waist heights; behind horse's
eye at intersection of grooves for inlaid bridle; between
horse's eyes on upper forehead.

Provenance: Charles L. Morley to Frederick M. Watkins,
1951; Bequest to the Fogg Art Museum, Harvard
University, 1972.52.

This repoussé relief is in an unusually fine state of preservation. Through skillful manipulation of the three-quarter view in very high relief, the artist has produced both a superb rendition of human and equine anatomy and an enhanced sense of depth. The young rider is nude except for his ankle-high laced shoes and the traveling cloak that billows out behind him. The stocky youth's broad shoulders and squarish, compartmentalized torso are patterned after the Polykleitan canon. The depression that marks his left nipple may have had a silver inlay. His cap-like hair, parted in the middle, falls in short locks over his forehead. His head, turned slightly to the left, affords both frontal and profile views. His genitalia are delicately modeled in relief, with faint incised lines on the inside of his thigh and above his groin.

The youth holds at waist height what appears to be a torch or bundle of foliage, marked by incised grooves, which disappears behind the horse's head. His left arm seems to pass behind the horse's mane. The cloak, covered with minute punctate dots, curves behind his head, thus heightening the three-dimensional effect of the relief.

The horse seems small in proportion to the rider. Its head and body are executed in high repoussé. Its mane is a closely cropped crest, reminiscent of those on some of the horses from the Parthenon frieze. Rendered in short, undulating incised strokes, it culminates in a bunched topknot behind the ears. The right ear is laid back slightly, adding to the vitality infused by the thick, parted lips and flaring nostrils. Grooves into which the bridle was inlaid pass around the horse's muzzle just above the nostrils and behind the eyes; the upper channel is intersected by looping grooves that pass behind the ears. Additional channels for inlay run down the right side of the head and the top of the muzzle.

The horse's head, turned outward as if responding to pressure from the reins, presses against the neck; wrinkles are incised in the depression between neck and jaw. Other delicate incisions for hair occur in the concavity between body and thigh, and on the underbelly where two raised veins are depicted. Details of the underside of the right front hoof are incised as well. The rider sits on a panther (?) skin covered with fine short incisions indicating fur. The rear leg and foot of the skin, which hangs in an S-curve down the horse's thigh, are rendered in relief, while its front foot, passing behind the horse's upraised front leg, is executed completely by incision. The skin passes around the front of the horse's neck in a narrow band that widens into two points in the middle of its chest. This band is decorated by short S-shaped incisions.

No exact parallels or antecedents for this unusual appliqué are known to this writer. The edges are not entirely smooth and flat, as one would expect of a repoussé relief from a mirror case (cf. W. Züchner, *Griechische Klappspiegel* [Berlin, 1942], passim). It does not curve enough to have been the base plate of the vertical handle for a large, ornate hydria (cf. No. 2). Perhaps it was a decorative appliqué for a chest or other piece of furniture, or an ornament for an elaborate cuirass or helmet.

A miniature descendant of the horsemen of the Parthenon frieze and such later reliefs as the grave monument in Athens of Dexileos, killed in 394 B.C. (R. Lullies and M. Hirmer, *Greek Sculpture* [New York, 1960], pl. 192), this rider may be taking part in a ritual of some kind, as suggested by the pelt and torch-like object. A hero is proposed as the subject in Morley's note on the bill of sale to Professor Watkins, in which he mentions identification of the piece by Prof. (Ludwig?) Curtius as one of the Dioskouroi. The abundant, discrete metal inlays and the exquisite but studious modeling suggest that this is a Roman version of a classical motif, subtly rendered by a classicizing workshop perhaps in Greece or Asia Minor. One may suggest a date early in the second century A.D., possibly during the reign of Hadrian (117-138 A.D.).

DGM

Bibliography: Unpublished.

37

Horse and Female Rider

Chinese, T'ang Dynasty, 618-906 A.D.

Pottery, L. 12¾ in. (0.325 m.)

Pinkish clay. Unglazed; pigments not fired. Horse's hollow belly is perforated by a one-inch square hole. Rider broken at waist and repaired. Horse's legs show multiple breaks; piece missing from r. front leg; tail broken and repaired. Body of horse coated with brick-red pigment; traces of white pigment on l. side of horse's head, saddle-cloth, hooves; traces of gray on saddle. Face and neck of rider covered by gray-white wash; hair, eyes, eyebrows are blackish-gray; mouth is red. Collar of coat is brick-red, with traces of cinnabar on upper part of garment; lower part of trousers is black. Rider's face, grayish-white area on chest appear to be later repaint; most of white pigment on l. side of horse's head and on hooves is also later.

Provenance: Frederick M. Watkins; Bequest to the Fogg Art Museum, Harvard University, 1972.58.

The horse moves at a fast pace, his head turned to the left, his forelock blown back over his ears, and his mouth open. No trappings save the saddle and saddle-blanket are described. The rider, as evidenced by the arrangement of the hair in two topknots, is a woman. That she is dressed as a man, with a long coat, trousers and boots, should come as no surprise, for such garb was apparently an established fashion for women riders in eighth-century China. At the time of the Emperor Ming-huang, who ascended the throne in 713, "the palace maids who followed the imperial carriage on horseback mostly wore *hu* hats, and exposed their prettily painted faces. The common people emulated them, and the *wei-mao* [sun-bonnet] fashion was absolutely out. After a while they did not use any headcovering when riding, and some wore men's clothes and boots; highborn and lowborn, men and women—all looked alike." (Hsiang Ta, *T'ang-tai Ch'ang-an yü hsi-yü wen-ming,* as translated in J. G. Mahler, *The Westerners Among the Figurines of the T'ang Dynasty of China* [Rome, 1959], 111). The posture and dress of the rider and the movement of her mount suggest that the figure represents a woman playing polo, a game popular among both men and women at the T'ang court. A set of four female polo players very similar to the Watkins example is in the collection of the Nelson Gallery-

Atkins Museum in Kansas City (Mahler, 111 and pl. 30, and Fine Arts Exhibition Expo 67, *Man and His World,* [Montreal, 1967], 100-101, no. 48).

The Watkins rider clearly differs from the short-waisted, more softly modeled female riders of early T'ang; her mount, in contrast to those of early T'ang, is a more substantial creature with a powerful neck and a more fleshed-out appearance achieved through an improved integration of the various parts of the body (compare, for example, equestriennes excavated from a tomb at Yang-t'ou-chen, Hsi-an, Shensi, dated 668; *Wen-wu,* 1959/3, 45-53, fig. 28). In comparison to the present horse, those of the mid-T'ang period, such as one in the British Museum from the tomb of Liu T'ing-hsün, who died in 728 (William B. Honey, *The Ceramic Art of China* [London, 1945], 43-44, pl. 16c), are already stylistically more advanced and more naturalistically modeled, with particular attention to the muscles of the chest and upper part of the legs.

The attire of the Watkins rider, her coat with folded-back collar, her hair combed into two closely placed topknots, the general description of her body—slender, long-waisted, and round-faced—and the proportioning of her mount, with stress on the broad arched neck and the head relatively large in relation to the rest of the body, agree closely with a series of mounted figures excavated in 1958 from a tomb at Nan-li-wang-ts'un near Ch'ang-an, Shensi, dated to 706 (see *Wen-wu,* 1959/8, 8-18, fig. 6). Thus the Watkins group can be dated to the turn of the eighth century on the basis of stylistic as well as literary evidence.

LGFH

Bibliography: Unpublished.

38

Bactrian Horse

Chinese, T'ang Dynasty, 618-906 A.D.

Pottery, H. 14 in. (0.36 m.); L. of base 6¼ in. (0.16 m.)

Gray clay. Unglazed; pigments not fired. Belly is hollow; irregular oval-shaped opening under belly. Tip of tail broken off; vertical crack on l. front leg; r. hind leg broken and repaired. Buff wash covers body of horse, saddle-blanket. Dark gray: mane, tail, saddle, harness; streaks on saddle-blanket and under eyes. Cinnabar pigment outlines eyes, mouth; red ochre on muzzle, hooves, outer folds of saddle-cloth; center of saddle-cloth is vermilion. Palmette-shaped trappings on hindquarters and chest show traces of red and green paint.

Provenance: Frederick M. Watkins; Bequest to the Fogg Art Museum, Harvard University, 1972.327.

This magnificent Bactrian steed stands with his hind legs bent, his haunches considerably lower than his withers, and his right foreleg raised. The neck is arched and twisted to the left; the head is bent down and turned leftward. The spiritedness of the beast is further expressed by the prominent eyes, open mouth, and protruding nostrils. His mane and saddle-cloth are blown back as if by the wind. The series of six palmette-shaped trappings on the hindquarters and the three on the chest, as well as the rosette-shaped ornament with pearl border on the horse's back are all of Sassanian type.

Sculptural depictions of Bactrian horses are known as early as the Han Dynasty (206 B.C.–220 A.D.). The most recent and surely the most spectacular finds of this period are a number of horses in varying poses—in this case cast in bronze—discovered in 1969 at Wu-wei in the eastern province of Kansu and dating from the Eastern Han (250-220 A.D.; see *Wen wu* 1972/2, 16-24, color pl. 1 and pls. 5-7, and *Historical Relics Unearthed in New China* [Peking, 1972], pl. 110). By contrast to those of Han, T'ang horses appear to be of more ample proportions; in particular the breadth of the neck is increased and the legs are heavier-set. The lithesome vigor of the Han horse, suggestive of its speed, is replaced in its T'ang counterpart by a sense of power and monumentality gained through the imposing weightiness of its presence. By the mid-eighth century this stress on monumentality resulted in more naturalistic but also more static representations, quite unlike the present example. Compared to

dated examples of T'ang horses, the Watkins piece most nearly resembles those from a tomb located east of Hsi-an, Shensi, dating roughly between 713 and 740 (*Wen-wu ts'an-k'ao tzu-liao*, 1956/8, 33-39, figs. 3-4), and may be dated to the early eighth century.

LGFH

Bibliography: Unpublished.

39

Lady Musician

Chinese, T'ang Dynasty, 618-906 A.D.

Pottery, H. 6¾ in. (0.17 m.); W. of base 4¼ in. (0.11 m.)

Buff clay with coating of chalky pinkish-white clay wash. Unglazed; pigments not fired; interior hollow. Eyes, eyebrows and mouth possibly repainted. Black painting on hair; traces of brown on bodice; traces of cinnabar on sleeves; red ochre in folds of skirt.

Provenance: Frederick M. Watkins; Bequest to the Fogg Art Museum, Harvard University, 1972.59.

The figure, seated with her legs folded to the side, holds a Pan-pipe to her lips. Her close-fitting garment with long tight sleeves is in the Tocharian mode, fashionable in China during the seventh and eighth centuries (see J. G. Mahler, *The Westerners Among the Figurines of the T'ang Dynasty of China* [Rome, 1959], 108). Her coiffure, parted in the center and worked up into two large topknots, is derived from Kuchā and was popular in China as early as the Sui Dynasty (589-618 A.D.; see Mahler, 109-110).

No doubt this musician originally belonged with a larger group of figures which would have been placed in a tomb to provide entertainment for the deceased in the nether world. Such groups of musician figures were familiar at least as early as the Han period (206 B.C.- 220 A.D.); perhaps the most noteworthy are the wooden figures excavated this year from the remarkable tomb, dated to the first half of the second century, at Ma-wang- tui near Ch'ang-sha in Hunan (see *China Reconstructs,* 21:9 [September, 1972], 20-23). From the Sui Dynasty comes one of the most complete sets of seated musicians; in the tomb of Chang Sheng in the vicinity of An-yang, Honan and dated A.D. 595, were found eight figures playing such instruments as the *p'i-li* (Barbarian flute), *k'ung-hou* (a harp-like lute), *p'i-p'a* (lute), *pa* (cymbals) and *hsiao* (Pan-pipe) (see *K'ao-ku,* 1959/10, 541-545, fig. 2, nos. 2 and 3, pl. 10, figs. 1-6, and *Historical Relics Unearthed in New China* [Peking, 1972], pl. 136).

Although the Watkins musician resembles those from the Sui tomb in posture—seated with feet to the side on a square base—it is more sculptural in nature, with more attention given to anatomical structure. In the Watkins figure the garment clings to the body instead of falling straight from the waist to the base; the position of the thighs is clearly revealed. The skirt forms gracious folds around the base, whereas in the less sophisticated Sui figures the skirt blends into the base itself. The face of the Watkins figure is more refined, the nose more slender and the eyes and mouth more delicate. On the other hand, it has not yet attained the strongly expressive and almost portrait-like quality of figures of the mid-T'ang period (see, for instance, heads excavated from P'an-liu-ts'un, Hsi-an, Shensi, dated to 757; *Wen-wu ts'an-k'ao tzu-liao,* 1958/10, 40-41, figs. 1-3). The Watkins musician, which in physiognomy and hair style most closely resembles a head from a tomb at Yang-t'ou-chen, Hsi-an, Shensi, dated 688 (*Wen-wu,* 1959/3, 43-53, fig. 25), may be dated to the late seventh or early eighth century. A set of seated musicians similar in appearance, known to have come from Lo-yang, Honan (see Ch'in T'ing-yü, ed., *Chung-kuo ku-tai t'ao-su i-shu* [Peking, 1957], pl. 53), would appear to date from the same period.

LGFH

Bibliography: Unpublished.

40

Figurine

Maya, type from Jaina Island and vicinity, Campeche region of western Yucatan, late 7th to early 8th century A.D.

Terra cotta, H. 7⅜ in. (0.187 m.); W. 2¹¹⁄₁₆ in. (0.069 m.)

Intact. Fine-textured, reddish-brown clay. Assembled from hand-modeled parts; face molded; body hollow, smoothed by fingers of artisan. Hole in back, below right shoulder. Traces of white color (paint?) on headdress and protected parts of body and costume.

Provenance: Frederick M. Watkins; Bequest to the Fogg Art Museum, Harvard University, 1972.60.

This exquisitely modeled figurine depicts a seated priest or other member of the Maya ruling elite. His arms are folded across his chest, right hand above the left. The fingers of his right hand are incised; only the thumb of his left hand is separately modeled. He wears a skirt or kilt, with a prominent sash made from a narrow sheet of clay on the left side, tapering toward the waist. A similar sheet of clay projects as a loin cloth from beneath his kilt and falls over his stumpy crossed legs. There is a groove at waist level around his back. Suspended from a cord of clay around his neck is a bar-like object with six small clay balls along the bottom edge. He wears an elaborate headdress, fashioned as a deer's head. The eye, eyebrow, and nostril of the deer's head are clay pellets, applied and smoothed; the mouth is incised. Other, larger clay balls were added to the deer's neck. The man's costume is completed by earspools, added as separate clay discs. The figure's convex, elongated face, with oval eyes and lips parted to reveal the upper teeth, is mold-made.

Most of the hollow Jaina-type figurines are fashioned to serve as whistles or rattles. The Watkins figure has a hole in the back and a deep puncture in the right shoulder made while the clay was still moist. When one blows into the slit in the right shoulder, the figurine emits a low note.

These statuettes are the finest terra cotta figurines made anywhere in the area occupied by the late classic phase of Maya civilization (Chiapas and Yucatan, Mexico; Guatemala; British Honduras and northern Honduras). Few have so far been found in controlled excavations; all indications, however, point to their manufacture as funerary offerings for graves on Jaina Island and the immediately adjacent part of Campeche, the western coastal area of the Yucatan peninsula, a region which appears to have had a special sanctity or attraction as a place of burial. For a headdress with deer's head similar to that worn by our figurine, see an incised shell plaque in Cleveland (inv. no. 65.550; "The Cleveland Museum of Art," *Archaeology,* 19 [1966], 282). Note also the animal-head headdresses worn by standing dignitaries in a wall painting in Room 2, Bonampak, Chiapas (H. Lehmann, "Middle American Protohistory," *McGraw-Hill Encyclopedia of World Art,* 10 [New York, 1965], cols. 36-38, pl. 55, bottom. On the symbolism of deer in Maya art and religion, see D. M. Pendergast, "The Actun Balam Vase," *Archaeology,* 19 [1966], 154-166 [reference courtesy of P. D. Shaplin]).

DGM

Bibliography: Unpublished. For Jaina figurines in general, see L.A.A. de Anda and G. F. Ekholm, "Clay Sculpture from Jaina; Island Burial Site Yields Maya Treasures," *Natural History,* 75 (1966), 40-47 (reference courtesy of T. Proskouriakoff and C. Coggins); also R. L. Rands, in R. Wauchope, ed., *Handbook of Middle American Indians,* II:1 (Austin, 1965), 535-560 (reference courtesy of P. D. Shaplin); R. Piña Chan, "Jaina Campeche," Mexico City, Inst. Nac. de Antrop. e Hist., Bol. 16 (1964) (reference courtesy of T. Proskouriakoff); idem, *Jaina* (Mexico City, 1968), (reference courtesy of P. D. Shaplin). In addition to the colleagues cited above, I wish to thank Miss Tatiana Proskouriakoff for help in dating the figurine and Mrs. Rose Marie Mitten for reference help.

41

Rhyton with Boar's Head

Forgery, perhaps made in Greece before 1900 A.D., imitating Greek (Tarentine) rhyta of the 4th-3rd centuries B.C.

H. 4¹¹⁄₁₆ in. (0.12 m.); L. 6¾ in. (0.169 m.)

Provenance: Viscount Allenby; Frederick M. Watkins; Gift to the Fogg Art Museum, Harvard University, 1959.190.

Herbert Hoffmann has delineated the "Duck-Boar Group" of forgeries of Tarentine rhyta, to which both this vessel and No. 43 belong. They must have been produced before 1912, when a boar's head rhyton very similar to this example is recorded in the Lambros-Dattari Sale (*Collection de feu M. Jean P. Lambros* [Athens] *et de M. Giovanni Dattari* [Cairo], [Paris, Hôtel Drouot, June 30-July 2, 1921], no. 270, pl. 23). Hoffmann feels that "there are indications that the group antedates the turn of the century"; he points out that rhyta were enthusiastically collected during the *Art Nouveau* period and that most known forgeries of rhyta date from that era. Hoffmann also indicates that although he has not identified the workshop that produced these forgeries, it is more likely to have been in Greece than in Italy.

Among the stylistic criteria that condemn this group of vessels, Hoffmann points out that their form is based on metal rather than ceramic prototypes and that the narrow handle, canted on the outside, is unlike any known type of Greek vase handle. Similar boar's head rhyta include two in the Römisch-Germanisches Zentralmuseum, Mainz; the boars' heads on these, the Lambros-Dattari example, and the Watkins rhyton may well have been made from the same mold.

SD

Bibliography: H. Hoffmann, *Tarentine Rhyta* (Mainz, 1966), 131-132, with bibl. on comparanda; cf. pl. 62, 1.

42

Rhyton with Duck's Head

Forgery, perhaps made in Greece before 1900 A.D., imitating Greek (Tarentine) rhyta of the 4th-3rd centuries B.C.

H. 4⅛ in. (0.103 m.); L. 7⁹⁄₁₆ in. (0.194 m.)

Provenance: Frederick M. Watkins; Gift to the Fogg Art Museum, Harvard University, 1959.191.

Like the preceding rhyton, this is a member of the "Duck-Boar Group" of forgeries. Other examples, detailed by Hoffmann, are two in Brussels, one in the Musée des Beaux-arts, Montreal, and one in the National Museum in Athens.

SD

Bibliography: H. Hoffmann, *Tarentine Rhyta* (Mainz, 1966), 131-132, with bibl. on comparanda; cf. pl. 62, 2.

43

Warrior

Etruscan (?), ca. 450-420 B.C. (?)

Bronze, H. excluding pin in r. foot 5⅜ in. (0.135 m.)

Solid cast. Mottled green-brown patina. Partial analysis by x-ray fluorescence in 1971 showed the metal to contain about 10-12% tin, 2% zinc, 2.5% lead. Missing l. arm, l. foot, end(s) of staff or spear.

Provenance: Frederick M. Watkins; Gift to the Fogg Art Museum, Harvard University, 1961.143.

Numerous Etruscan bronze statuettes of warriors have been found. They served both as dedications to the gods before or after battle, and as adornments of vessels and utensils. Many stride militantly with spears poised. This figure, however, stands at ease. He wears the costume of the Greek fifth-century hoplite: a plumed Attic helmet with its hinged cheek pieces turned up, a short-skirted *chiton* beneath a cuirass that ends in a double row of rectangular flaps *(pteryges)*, and greaves. The scale pattern on the cuirass represents the overlapping rounded metal plates that were stitched onto these leather garments to afford the wearer greater protection. He holds a portion of a spear or staff. Most Etruscan warriors hold long-handled spears, but here the unusual cupping of the hand beneath the extant portion makes such a reconstruction improbable.

The artistic predilection for fine linear detailing revealed in the careful cold-working of the body armor is evident also in the striations of the helmet plume, the delicate rendering of hair, beard, and sideburns, and the minute cross-hatching of the *pteryges*.

The stocky proportions of the warrior and his facial features—wide-open almond-shaped eyes, prominent arched eyebrows, small mouth with a hint of an "archaic smile," and small rounded chin—find their closest parallels among statuettes made at Vulci, a major Etruscan bronze-working center.

The figurine is extremely close in type and pose to a candelabrum figure from Marzabotto (Giglioli, *AE,* pl. 252:1,3), although in the latter the cold-working is even more elaborate and the facial features are less archaic. The Marzabotto warrior has his left arm around the shoulders of a woman, who pours an offering for his safe return. The missing arm of the Watkins piece might have made such a gesture.

Several factors have cast doubt on the authenticity of the Watkins statuette. Its very similarity to the Marzabotto piece is cause for suspicion. Most classical bronzes were cast in the lost-wax process, in which the wax model and the clay mold must both be destroyed in making the finished bronze. (For an explanation of this process, see A. Steinberg, "Techniques of Working Bronze," in Fogg, *Master Bronzes,* 9-11). Originality was highly prized among ancient craftsmen, and only in the case of pairs of handles or sets of vessel feet does one usually find "matching" bronzes, where the artist has made two or more wax originals as similar to each other as possible. Some interesting exceptions occur among warrior statuettes, however. E. H. Richardson has recently isolated a group of elongated warriors bearing a distinct family resemblance, which were produced in an Umbrian workshop in the mid-fifth century B.C. ("The Icon of the Heroic Warrior: A Study in Borrowing," in D. G. Mitten, J. G. Pedley, and J. A. Scott, eds., *Studies Presented to George M. A. Hanfmann* [Cambridge, Mass., 1971], 161-168).

H. Jucker, who has verbally doubted the Watkins piece on stylistic grounds, discovered on the art market a bronze replica of the woman from the Marzabotto group, which he feels sure is modern. Its metal includes about one per cent zinc. As reported above, the Watkins bronze also includes enough zinc to suggest that it was deliberately added to the alloy. With the exception of some high-zinc metal produced at Gordion from unusual local ores, it is generally believed that the ancients did not master the use of highly volatile zinc in metal-working until the Roman period. Comparatively few Etruscan bronzes have been scientifically analyzed, however, so that generalizations about metallic content are necessarily tentative. The amounts of lead and tin in the Watkins piece are within the range of known Etruscan bronzes.

Examination of a polished cross-section of a small sample from the helmet crest of the Watkins bronze revealed a lack of intercrystalline penetration of the corrosion layers into the body metal. In several areas cuprous oxide occurs on top of other corrosion products, rather than immediately above the metal as would be expected. These factors, in addition to the presence of a modern zinc pigment, "chrome green," suggest that the patina was artificially induced.

SD

Bibliography: FAM Acquisitions, 1959-62, 31, ill. p. 142; Teitz, *Etruscan,* 75, no. 64, ill. p. 163; S. Doeringer and G. M. A. Hanfmann, "An Etruscan Bronze Warrior in the Fogg Museum," *StEtr,* 35 (1967), 645-653, pls. 139-142; S. Doeringer, "An Etruscan Warrior in the Fogg Art Museum," *Art Quarterly,* 30 (1967), 31-38, figs. 1-8; Fogg, *Master Bronzes,* 172, no. 173, ill. On the late classical style of Vulcian bronzes, see S. Haynes, "Etruscan Bronzes in the British Museum: New Acquisitions and Old Possessions," in *Art and Technology,* 177-193. On zinc, at Gordion and in Roman alloys, see the discussion, pl. 55 of the same volume; and L. K. Congdon, "The Mantua Apollo of the Fogg Art Museum," *AJA,* 67 (1963), 8-9, with bibl.

Ancient Coins

The coins in Frederick M. Watkins's bequest to the Fogg Art Museum represent more than a collector's connoisseurship, for within their compass it is possible to review the achievements of ancient art in the medium of coinage. The collection achieves this documentary value not only because it includes outstanding examples of recognized masterpieces, such as the facing Apollo executed by Herakleides for Katane (No. 27) and the Naxian Dionysos head by the Aitna Master (No. 31), but also because of the exceptional artistic quality and state of preservation of each specimen selected by Professor Watkins for his cabinet.

The visitor and student can study here, side by side, coins illustrating the major artistic phases and movements in ancient coinage. The boldly modeled types of the early mints of Greece are represented by coins from such sites as Akanthos, Athens, Eretria, and Andros. The collection also contains examples of the incuse style of South Italy. These reflect the coin type's origin as an official seal, since one side is marked with a relief image while the other bears the seal-like incuse of the coin type. It also includes the eclectic representations of the Ionian coinages in gold and electrum, coins that emphasize the proximity of the die-cutter and the gem-engraver. Examples from the mints of the Peloponnesos reflect the formal cast of the fifth century art of this area. The best work of the school of master die-cutters of Katane in the last quarter of the fifth century is represented by Herakleides and Euainetos; the school was soon active at Syracuse, where Euainetos and Kimon created the style that was to be the most powerful influence in numismatic art of the fourth century. Finally, in the Watkins collection one can review portraits from the Hellenistic world and the Roman Empire.

R. Ross Holloway
*Professor of Central Mediterranean Archaeology,
Brown University*

Compiler's Note

In the catalogue entries the Greek and Roman scripts have been regularized. Legends known to exist on a particular die are omitted if there is no trace of them on the Watkins specimen. Legends only partially visible are given in full. A bibliographical reference marked with an asterisk is a complete die study of a mint or series in which the dies of the Watkins example have been identified. The descriptions of types have been compressed as far as possible. In the time available for the preparation of this catalogue it has not been possible to trace the pedigrees of the coins. Much information on this aspect of the collection, from Professor Watkins's notes, is on file at the Fogg Art Museum.

Numismatic Abbreviations

Obv.	obverse
Rev.	reverse
AR	silver
AV	gold
EL	electrum

Bibliographic Abbreviations

Babelon
E. Babelon, *Traité des monnaies grecques et romaines, deuxième partie, description historique* (Paris, 1910).

BMC
H. Mattingly et al., *Coins of the Roman Empire in the British Museum* (London, 1923-).

Brett
A. B. Brett, *Museum of Fine Arts, Boston, A Catalogue of Greek Coins* (Boston, 1955).

Hunterian
A. S. Robertson, *Roman Imperial Coins in the Hunter Coin Cabinet, University of Glasgow* (London, 1962-).

RIC
H. Mattingly, E. Sydenham, et al., *The Roman Imperial Coinage* (London, 1923-).

Rizzo
G. E. Rizzo, *Monete Greche della Sicilia* (Rome, 1946).

SNG Berry
Sylloge Nummorum Graecorum, The Burton Y. Berry Collection (New York, 1961-1962).

SNG Copenhagen
Sylloge Nummorum Graecorum, The Royal Collection in the Danish Museum 30 vols. (Copenhagen, 1942-1948).

SNG Lockett
Sylloge Nummorum Graecorum, The Lockett Collection (London, 1957).

SNG Oxford
Sylloge Nummorum Graecorum, Ashmolean Museum, Oxford, Parts I and II, (London, 1962 and 1969).

Abbreviations for periodicals follow the *American Journal of Archaeology*, 74 (1970), 3-8.

Calabria

1

Taras

AR stater, 510-490 B.C.

Obv. ΤΑΡΑΣ Phalanthos

Rev. ΤΑΡΑΣ Winged hippocamp. Shell.

Wt: 8.11 gm. (↖)

Bibliography: H. A. Cahn, "Early Tarentine Chronology," *Essays in Greek Coinage Presented to Stanley Robinson* (Oxford, 1968), 59-74.

2

Taras

AR stater, 430-420 B.C.

Obv. Phalanthos. Crayfish.

Rev. Phalanthos. Bird.

Wt: 7.70 gm. (↗)

Bibliography: A. J. Evans, "The Horsemen of Tarentum," *NC,* 3rd series, 9 (1889), 1-228, Period I.

3

Taras

AR stater, 420-380 B.C.

Obv. Horseman.

Rev. ΤΑΡΑΣ. Phalanthos. Ͱ.

Wt: 7.68 gm. (↘)

Bibliography: Evans, Period II.

4

Taras

AR stater, 380-345 B.C.

Obv. Horseman. A.

Rev. ΤΑΡΑΣ. Phalanthos. P.

Wt: 7.79 gm. (↖)

Bibliography: Evans, Period III.

5

Taras

AR stater, 380-345 B.C.

Obv. Horseman.

Rev. ΤΑΡΑΣ. Phalanthos.

Wt: 7.80 gm. (→)

Bibliography: Evans, Period III.

6

Taras

AR stater, 334-302 B.C.

Obv. Horseman. Victory bearing crown. ΣΙ. ΛΥΜΑ.

Rev. ΤΑΡΑΣ. Phalanthos. ΥΤ.

Wt: 6.41 gm. (↑)

Bibliography: Evans, Period V

7

Taras

AR stater, 235-228 B.C.

Obv. Horseman crowned by Victory. ΠΕΚ ligature. ΚΑΛΛΙΚΡΑΤΗΣ.

Rev. ΤΑΡΑΣ. Phalanthos. ΑΝΕ ligature.

Wt: 6.52 gm. (↘)

Bibliography: Evans, Period IX.

Lucania

8

Heraklea

AR stater, ca. 400 B.C.

Obv. Head of Athene. ΔΚΦ

Rev. ΗΡΑΚΛΗΙΩΝ. Herakles wrestling lion. Owl. ΚΑΛ.

Wt: 7.93 gm. (↙)

Bibliography: E. Work, *The Earlier Staters of Heraclea Lucaniae, ANSNNM,* 91 (New York, 1940), no. 35.*

9

Laos

AR stater, ca. 520 B.C.

Obv. ΛΑΓ Ι. Manheaded bull.

Rev. ΝΟΣ. Manheaded bull (incuse).

Wt: 7.07 gm. (↑)

Bibliography: SNG Oxford, no. 643.

10

Metapontum

AR stater, ca. 520 B.C.

Obv. META. Ear of wheat.

Rev. Ear of wheat (incuse).

Wt: 8.11 gm. (↑)

Bibliography: S. P. Noe, *The Coinage of Metapontum,* Part One, *ANSNNM,* 32 (New York, 1927), no. 134.*

11

Metapontum

AR stater, ca. 425 B.C.

Obv. Head of Persephone.

Rev. META. Ear of wheat.

Wt: 7.32 gm. (↑)

Bibliography: S. P. Noe, *The Coinage of Metapontum,* Part Two, *ANSNNM,* 47 (New York, 1931), no. 367.*

12

Poseidonia

AR stater, ca. 520 B.C.

Obv. ΠΟΣ. Poseidon.

Rev. ΠΟΣ. Poseidon (incuse).

Wt: 7.39 gm. (↑)

Bibliography: SNG Oxford, no. 815-816.

13

Thurioi

AR stater, ca. 430 B.C.

Obv. Head of Athene.

Rev. ΘΟΥΡΙΩΝ. Butting bull. Fish.

Wt: 7.71 gm. (↑)

Bibliography: SNG Oxford, no. 912.

14

Thurioi

AR stater, ca. 400 B.C.

Obv. Head of Athene.

Rev. ΘΟΥΡΙΩΝ. Butting bull. Fish.

Wt: 7.69 gm. (↑)

Bibliography: SNG Oxford, no. 928-961.

15

Velia

AR drachm, ca. 500 B.C.

Obv. Forepart of lion devouring prey.

Rev. Incuse.

Wt: 3.90 gm.

Bibliography: SNG Oxford, no. 1074-1078.

16

Velia

AR stater, ca. 400 B.C.

Obv. Head of Athene. P.

Rev. ΥΕΛΗΙΩΝ. Lion. Φ. P.

Wt: 7.41 gm. (↘)

Bibliography: SNG Oxford, no. 1196.

Brettium

17

Kaulonia

AR stater, ca. 520 B.C.

Obv. ΚΑΥΛ. Apollo. Stag.

Rev. Apollo. Stag. (Incuse).

Wt: 8.21 gm. (↑)

Bibliography: S. P. Noe, *The Coinage of Caulonia*, Numismatic Studies, 9 (New York, 1958), no. 2.*

18

Rhegion

AR tetradrachm, 494-480 B.C.

Obv. Lion's protome.

Rev. ΡΕΓΙΝΟΝ. Calf's head.

Wt: 17.64 gm. (→)

Bibliography: Babelon, no. 2190. For the date, E.S.G. Robinson, "Rhegion, Zankle-Messana and the Samians," *JHS,* 66 (1946), 13-20.

19

Terina

AR stater, 420-400 B.C.

Obv. ΤΕΡΙΝΑΙΟΝ. Head of Terina.

Rev. Victory. Dove.

Wt: 7.88 gm. (↖)

Bibliography: K. Regling, *Terina*, Sechsundsechzigstes Programm zum Winckelmannsfeste (Berlin, 1906), no. 64.*

20

Akragas

AR tetradrachm, ca. 450 B.C.

Obv. ΑΚΡΑΓΑΝΤΟΣ. Eagle.

Rev. Crab.

Wt: 17.29 gm. (↓)

Bibliography: SNG Oxford, no. 1688-1671.

21

Akragas

AR tetradrachm, ca. 410 B.C.

Obv. ΑΚΡΑΓΑΝΤΙΝΩΝ. Quadriga. Vine branch.

Rev. Two eagles clutching hare. Head of river god. ΣΤΡΑΤΩΝ.

Wt: 16.74 gm. (↑)

Bibliography: SNG Oxford, no. 1677.

22

Gela

AR didrachm, 490/485-480/475 B.C.

Obv. Horseman.

Rev. ΓΕΛΑ. Forepart of manheaded bull.

Wt: 8.64 gm. (←)

Bibliography: G. K. Jenkins, *The Coinage of Gela*, Antike Münzen und Geschnittene Steine, 2 (Berlin, 1970), no. 7.*

23

Gela

AR tetradrachm, 480/475-475/470 B.C.

Obv. Quadriga crowned by Victory.

Rev. ΓΕΛΑΣ. Forepart of manheaded bull.

Wt: 17.48 gm. (↘)

Bibliography: Jenkins, no. 172.*

24

Himera

AR didrachm, after 482 B.C.

Obv. HIMEPA. Cock.

Rev. Crab.

Wt: 8.70 gm. (↖)

Bibliography: SNG Oxford, no. 1762.

25

Himera

AR tetradrachm, ca. 460-450 B.C.

Obv. Biga. Palm branch. ΠΕΛΟΨ.

Rev. IMEPA. Nymph.

Wt: 17.42 gm. (↙)

Bibliography: F. Gutmann and W. Schwabacher, "Die Tetradrachmenprägung von Himera,"*Mitteilungen des Bayerischen Numismatischen Gesellschaft,* 47 (1929), 101-144, no. 13.*

26

Katane

AR tetradrachm, ca. 450 B.C.

Obv. Biga crowned by Victory. Crayfish.

Rev. KATANAION. Head of Apollo. Fish.

Wt: 17.27 gm. (↓)

Bibliography: Rizzo, pl. 11, no. 17.

27

Katane

AR tetradrachm, ca. 410 B.C.

Obv. Head of Apollo. ΗΡΑΚΛΕΙΔΑΣ (at r.)

Rev. KATANAIΩN. Quadriga crowned by Victory. Fish.

Wt: 17.51 gm. (↘)

Bibliography: SNG Oxford, no. 1708; SNG Lockett, vol. 3, no. 730.

28

Katane

AR drachm, ca. 410 B.C.

Obv. KATANAIΩN. Quadriga, driver crowned by Victory.

Rev. Head of Amenanos. Two fish. Crayfish.

AMENANOΣ.

Wt: 4.18 gm. (→)

Bibliography: SNG Oxford, no. 1711.

29

Leontinoi

AR tetradrachm, ca. 475 B.C.

Obv. Quadriga, driver crowned by Victory. Lion.

Rev. ΛΕΟΝΤΙΝΟΝ. Head of Apollo. Three laurel leaves.

Lion.

Wt: 17.35 gm. (↘)

Bibliography: SNG Oxford, no. 1780. Related to the Damareteion series at Syracuse, an example of which is no. 39.

30

Leontinoi

AR tetradrachm, ca. 460 B.C.

Obv. Head of Apollo.

Rev. ΛΕΟΝΤΙΝΟΝ. Lion's head. Four wheat grains.

Wt: 17.11 gm. (↑)

Bibliography: SNG Oxford, no. 1781-1801.

31

Naxos

AR tetradrachm, 461 B.C.

Obv. Head of Dionysos.

Rev. NAXION. Silenus.

Wt: 16.80 gm. (↙)

Bibliography: H. A. Cahn, *Die Münzen der Sizilischen Stadt Naxos* (Basel, 1944), no. 54.*

32

Naxos

AR tetradrachm, 430-420 B.C.

Obv. Head of Dionysos.

Rev. NAΞION. Silenus. Ivy plant.

Wt: 17.03 gm. (↙)

Bibliography: Cahn, no. 101.*

33

Naxos

AR didrachm, 420-403 B.C.

Obv. NAΞIΩN. Head of Apollo. Laurel leaf.

Rev. Silenus. Ivy plant and herm. ΠΡΟΚΛΗΣ (on ground line).

Wt: 8.65 gm. (↙)

Bibliography: Cahn, no. 108.*

34

Messene

AR drachm, ca. 510 B.C.

Obv. ΔΑΝΚΛ. Dolphin in harbor.

Rev. Incuse. Shell (in center section).

Wt: 5.0 gm. (↗)

Bibliography: H. E. Gielow, "Die Silberprägung von Dankle-Massana," *Mitteilungen des Bayerischen Numismatischen Gesellschaft,* 48 (1930), 1-54, no. 23.

35

Messene

AR tetradrachm, ca. 410 B.C.

Obv. Biga of mules, driver crowned by Victory.

Two dolphins.

Rev. ΜΕΣΣΑΝΙΟΝ. Hare. Head of Pan

Wt: 17.20 gm. (↘)

Bibliography: SNG Oxford, no. 1848.

36

Segesta

AR didrachm, ca. 480 B.C.

Obv. Hound.

Rev. ΣΕΓΕΣΤΑΞΒΕΜΙ. Head of Segesta.

Wt: 8.67 gm. (⌐)

Bibliography: Brett, no. 311-312.

37

Selinus

AR tetradrachm, ca. 445 B.C.

Obv. ΣΕΛΙΝΟΝΤΙΟΝ. Quadriga with Apollo and Artemis.

Rev. ΣΕΛΙΝΟΣ. River god Selinos. Leaf. Bull on pedestal. Cock and altar.

Wt: 17.31 gm. (⌐)

Bibliography: W. Schwabacher, "Die Tetradrachmen-prägung von Selinunt," *Mitteilungen des Bayerischen Numismatischen Gesellschaft,* 43 (1925), 1-89, no. 11.*

38

Syracuse

AR tetradrachm, ca. 485 B.C.

Obv. Quadriga crowned by Victory.

Rev. ΣΥΡΑΚΟΣΙΟΝ. Head of Artemis – Arethusa surrounded by dolphins.

Wt: 17.06 gm. (⌐)

Bibliography: E. Boehringer, *Die Münzen von Syrakus* (Berlin, 1929), no. 57.*

39

Syracuse

AR tetradrachm, ca. 475 B.C.

Obv. Quadriga crowned by Victory. Lion.

Rev. ΣΥΡΑΚΟΣΙΟΝ. Head of Artemis – Arethusa surrounded by dolphins.

Wt: 17.39 gm. (✔)

Bibliography: Boehringer, *Syrakus,* no. 382*; C. Boehringer, "Hierons Aitna und das Hieroneion," *JfNG,* 17 (1968), 67-98. For discussion of the dating of this series, C.M. Kraay, *Greek Coins and History* (London, 1969), ch. 2.

40

Syracuse

AR tetradrachm, ca. 475 B.C.

Obv. Quadriga, driver crowned by Victory. Sea serpent.

Rev. ΣΥΡΑΚΟΣΙΟΝ. Head of Artemis – Arethusa surrounded by dolphins.

Wt: 17.10 gm. (✔)

Bibliography: Boehringer, *Syrakus,* no. 440.*

41

Syracuse

AR tetradrachm, ca. 460 B.C.

Obv. Quadriga, driver crowned by Victory. Sea serpent.

Rev. ΣΥΡΑΚΟΣΙΟΝ. Head of Artemis – Arethusa surrounded by dolphins.

Wt: 17.31 gm. (↘)

Bibliography: Boehringer, *Syrakus,* no. 492.*

42

Syracuse

AR tetradrachm, ca. 460 B.C.

Obv. Quadriga crowned by Victory. Sea serpent.

Rev. ΣΥΡΑΚΟΣΙΟΝ. Head of Artemis – Arethusa surrounded by dolphins.

Wt: 17.31 gm. (↓)

Bibliography: Boehringer, *Syrakus,* no. 514.*

43

Syracuse

AR tetradrachm, ca. 420-410 B.C.

Obv. Quadriga. Victory approaching with plaque inscribed ΕΥΑΙΝΕΤΟ. Two dolphins.

Rev. ΣΥΡΑΚΟΣΙΩΝ. Head of Artemis – Arethusa surrounded by dolphins. Below neck ΕΥΜΕΝΟΥ.

Wt: 16.71 gm. (↑)

Bibliography: L. Tudeer, "Die Tetradrachmenprägung von Syrakus in der Periode der signierenden Künstler," *ZfN,* 30 (1913), 1-292, no. 45.*

44

Syracuse

AR tetradrachm, ca. 410 B.C.

Obv. Quadriga, driver crowned by Victory. Wheat ear.

Rev. Head of Artemis – Arethusa surrounded by dolphins.

Wt: 17.16 gm. (↙)

Bibliography: Tudeer, no. 63.*

45

Syracuse

AR tetradrachm, ca. 410 B.C.

Obv. Head of Arethusa surrounded by dolphins. On hair band ΚΙΜΩΝ.

Rev. ΣΥΡΑΚΟΣΙΩΝ. Quadriga, driver crowned by Victory. Wheat ear.

Wt: 17.26 gm. (↘)

Bibliography: Tudeer, no. 78.

46

Syracuse

AV 100-litra piece, ca. 410 B.C.

Obv. ΣΥΡΑΚΟΣΙΩΝ. Head of Artemis – Arethusa. ΚΑ.

Rev. Herakles wrestling lion.

Wt: 5.83 gm. (↗)

Bibliography: G. de Ciccio, "Gli aurei siracusani di Cimone e di Eveneto," *Bollettino del Circolo Numismatico Napoletano*, 1-2 (1922), 3-27, no. 20.*

47

Syracuse

AR dekadrachm, ca. 410 B.C.

Obv. Quadriga, driver crowned by Victory. Panoply resting on step inscribed ΑΘΛΑ.

Rev. ΣΥΡΑΚΟΣΙΩΝ. Head of Artemis – Arethusa surrounded by dolphins. Below neck ΕΥΑΙΝΕ.

Wt: 43.00 gm. (↙)

Bibliography: A. Gallatin, *Syracusan Dekadrachms of the Euainetos Type* (Cambridge, Mass., 1930), no. C II.

48

Syracuse

AR dekadrachm, ca. 410 B.C.

Obv. Quadriga, driver crowned by Victory. Panoply.

Rev. ΣΥΡΑΚΟΣΙΩΝ. Head of Artemis – Arethusa surrounded by dolphins. On hair band ΚΙ.

Wt: 42.94 gm. (↓)

Bibliography: J. H. Jonkees, *The Kimonian Dekadrachm* (Utrecht, 1940), no. 1.

49

Syracuse

AR dekadrachm, ca. 410 B.C.

Obv. Quadriga, driver crowned by Victory. Panoply.

Rev. ΣΥΡΑΚΟΣΙΩΝ. Head of Artemis – Arethusa surrounded by dolphins. On dolphin below neck ΚΙΜΩΝ. On hair band Κ.

Wt: 43.35 gm. (↓)

Bibliography: Jonkees, no. 3.

50

Syracuse

AR dekadrachm, ca. 410 B.C.

Obv. Quadriga, driver crowned by Victory. Panoply resting on a step inscribed ΑΘΛΑ.

Rev. ΣΥΡΑΚΟΣΙΩΝ. Head of Artemis – Arethusa surrounded by dolphins.

Wt: 43.07 gm. (↗)

Bibliography: Jonkees, no. 12.

51

Syracuse

AV drachm, Agathokles, 317-310 B.C.

Obv. Head of Apollo.

Rev. ΣΥΡΑΚΟΣΙΩΝ. Biga. Triskeles.

Wt: 4.31 gm. (↙)

Bibliography: SNG Oxford, no. 2055-2056.

52

Syracuse

AR tetradrachm, Agathokles, 310-305 B.C.

Obv. Head of Persephone. ΚΟΡΑΣ.

Rev. ΑΓΑΘΟΚΛΕΙΟΣ. Victory erecting trophy. Α. Triskeles.

Wt: 17.03 gm. (↘)

Bibliography: SNG Oxford, no. 2074-2078.

Siculo – Punic

53

AR tetradrachm, ca. 390 B.C.

Obv. Female head surrounded by dolphins. Shell.

Rev. תנחמ םע (ammchnt). Horse's head and palm tree.

Wt: 17.04 gm. (↑)

Bibliography: SNG Oxford, no. 2159

Macedonia – Cities

54

Akanthos

AR tetradrachm, 500-480 B.C.

Obv. Lion ravening bull. Horns.

Rev. Incuse.

Wt: 17.21 gm.

Bibliography: J. Desneux, "Les tétradrachmes d'Akanthos," *RBN,* 95 (1949), 1-122, no. 3.*

55

Akanthos

AR tetradrachm, 424-380 B.C.

Obv. Lion ravening bull. ΑΛΕΞΙΟΣ.

Rev. ΑΚΑΝΘΙΟΝ. Field, in center
four squares with raised granulated surfaces.

Wt: 14.07 gm. (↑)

Bibliography: Desneux, no. 150.*
(citing this coin).

56

Mende

AR tetradrachm, 460-420 B.C.

Obv. Dionysos on donkey. Grasshopper.

Rev. MENΔAION. Vine.

Wt: 17.01 gm. (→)

Bibliography: S. P. Noe, *The Mende (Kaliandra) Hoard,* ANSNNM, 27 (New York, 1926), no. 90.*

57

Mende

AR tetradrachm, 460-420 B.C.

Obv. Dionysos on donkey. In exergue, caduceus and letters read by Noe as NIΣ.

Rev. MENΔAION. Vine.

Wt: 16.60 gm. (↙)

Bibliography: Noe, no. 93.*

58

Neapolis

AR stater, 500-480 B.C.

Obv. Gorgoneion.

Rev. Incuse.

Wt: 9.67 gm.

Bibliography: Brett, no. 557-561.

59

Terone

AR tetradrachm, 520-480 B.C.

Obv. Amphora.

Rev. Incuse.

Wt: 16.73 gm.

Bibliography: H. Gaebler, *Die Antiken Münzen Nord-Griechenlands,* vol. 3, pt. 2, *Die Antiken Münzen von Makedonia und Pannonia* (Berlin, 1935), 114, no. 1.

60

Chalkidian League

AR tetradrachm, 379-376 B.C.

Obv. Head of Apollo.

Rev. ΧΑΛΚΙΔΕΩΝ. Lyre ΚΡΑ. ΕΠΙ ΑΣΚΛΗΠΙΟΔΩΡΟ.

Wt: 14.39 gm. (↓)

Bibliography: D. M. Robinson and P. A. Clement, *The Chalcidic Mint and the Excavation Coins Found in 1928-1934,* Excavations at Olynthos, pt. 9 (Baltimore, 1938), no. 86.* Mint of Olynthos.

61

Chalkidian League

AR tetradrachm, 361-358 B.C.

Obv. Head of Apollo.

Rev. ΧΑΛΚΙΔΕΩΝ. Lyre. ΕΠΙ ΟΛΥΜΠΙΧΟΥ.

Wt: 13.98 gm. (↑)

Bibliography: Robinson and Clement, no. 115.* Mint of Olynthos.

62

Chalkidian League

AR tetradrachm, 355-352 B.C.

Obv. Head of Apollo.

Rev. ΧΑΛΚΙΔΕΩΝ. Lyre. ΕΠΙ ΑΡΙΣΤΩΝΟΣ.

Wt: 14.22 gm. (↖)

Bibliography: Robinson and Clement, no. 128.* Mint of Olynthos.

63

Derrones

AR octodrachm, 520-480 B.C.

Obv. Ox-drawn chariot with seated driver. Helmet.

Rev. Triskeles surrounded by rosettes.

Wt: 38.70 gm.

Bibliography: J. N. Svoronos, *L'Hellénisme primitif de la Macédoine* (Athens and Paris, 1919), 9, no. 17.

64

Philip II, 359-336 B.C.

AR tetradrachm.

Obv. Head of Zeus.

Rev. ΦΙΛΙΠΠΟΥ. Horseman. Wreath. Ξ and M.

Wt: 14.30 gm. (↗)

Bibliography: SNG Berry, no. 108-121.

65

Demetrios, 306-286 B.C.

AR tetradrachm.

Obv. Victory on prow of warship.

Rev. ΒΑΣΙΛΕΩΣ ΔΗΜΗΤΡΙΟΥ. Poseidon. HP ligature
and Ω and bipennis ligature.

Wt: 17.13 gm. (↑)

Bibliography: E. T. Newell, *The Coinages of Demetrios
Poliorcetes* (London, 1927), obv. XXI.
Issue of 300–295 B.C. Mint of Salamis, Cyprus.

66

Demetrios, 306-286 B.C.

AR drachm.

Obv. Head of Demetrios.

Rev. ΒΑΣΙΛΕΩΣ ΔΗΜΗΤΡΙΟΥ. Poseidon. Leaf.
HPA ligature.

Wt: 4.02 gm. (↑)

Bibliography: Newell, *Demetrios,* no. 55.* Issue of
301-295 B.C. Mint of Ephesus.

67

Antigonos II, Gonatas, 277-258 B.C.

AR tetradrachm.

Obv. Head of Pan in center of Macedonian shield.

Rev. ΒΑΣΙΛΕΩΣ ΑΝΤΙΓΟΝΟΥ. Athene. Helmet. HP ligature.

Wt: 17.13 gm. (↖)

Bibliography: SNG Berry, no. 354.

68

Philip V, 220-179 B.C.

AR tetradrachm.

Obv. Head of Philip.

Rev. ΒΑΣΙΛΕΩΣ ΦΙΛΙΠΠΟΥ. Athene. ΣΡ ligature and ΕΡ ligature.

Wt: 16.99 gm. (↑)

Bibliography: Brett, no. 716. Issue of 220-205 B.C.; C. Boehringer, *Zur Chronologie Mittelhellenistischer Münzserien 220-160 v. Chr.*, Antike Münzen und Geschnittene Steine, 5 (Berlin, 1972), 330 ff.

69

Perseus, 179-168 B.C.

AR tetradrachm.

Obv. Head of Perseus.

Rev. ΒΑΣΙΛΕΩΣ ΠΕΡΣΕΩΣ. Eagle on thunderbolt in oak wreath. ΑΥ ligature, HP ligature and ΑΝ.

Wt: 16.97 gm. (↑)

Bibliography: Brett, no. 720-722. Issue of 173-171 B.C.; Boehringer, *Chronologie*, 101-102.

70

Abdera

AR tetradrachm, 473/70–449/8 B.C.

Obv. Griffin. Kantharos.

Rev. Field, in center four squares. ΕΠΙ ΣΜΟΡΔΟ ΤΟ ΡΜΟΚΑΛ (Thracian name and patronymic).

Wt: 15.00 gm. (←)

Bibliography: J. M. F. May, *The Coinage of Abdera,* ed. C. M. Kraay and G. K. Jenkins, The Royal Numismatic Society Special Publications, no. 6 (London, 1966), no. 138.*

71

Ainos

AR tetradrachm, 455–453 B.C.

Obv. Head of Hermes.

Rev. AINI. Goat. Herm on throne.

Wt: 16.55 gm. (↙)

Bibliography: J. M. F. May, *Ainos, Its History and Coinage* (Oxford, 1950), no. 71* (citing this coin).

72

Ainos

AR tetradrachm, 415–413 B.C.

Obv. Head of Hermes.

Rev. AIN. Goat. Ivy plant.

Wt: 16.05 gm. (↓)

Bibliography: May, *Ainos,* no. 244* (citing this coin).

73

Ainos

AR tetradrachm, 412-410 B.C.

Obv. Head of Hermes.

Rev. AINI. Goat. Caduceus.

Wt: 16.43 gm. (←)

Bibliography: May, *Ainos,* no. 258.*

74

Ainos

AR tetradrachm, 380-378 B.C.

Obv. Head of Hermes.

Rev. AINION. Goat. Star.

Wt: 15.63 gm. (↑)

Bibliography: May, *Ainos,* no. 392* (citing this coin).

Kingdom of Thrace

75

Lysimachos, 323-281 B.C.

AR tetradrachm.

Obv. Head of Alexander the Great with the horn of Ammon.

Rev. ΒΑΣΙΛΕΩΣ ΛΥΣΙΜΑΧΟΥ. Athene. Victory crowning the king's name. Torch.

Wt: 16.93 gm. (↑)

Bibliography: Brett, no. 823-839. Issue after 306 B.C. Attributed to the mint of Lampsacus in the trays of the American Numismatic Society.

Islands of Thrace

76

Thasos

AR stater, 500-465 B.C.

Obv. Silenos abducting nymph.

Rev. Incuse.

Wt: 8.96 gm.

Bibliography: Brett, no. 850-853.

77

Thasos

AR stater, ca. 440 B.C.

Obv. Silenos abducting nymph. A.

Rev. Incuse.

Wt: 8.68 gm.

Bibliography: Brett, no. 855.

78

Thasos

AR tetradrachm, 411-380 B.C.

Obv. Head of Dionysos.

Rev. ΘΑΣΙΟΝ. Herakles shooting. Jug.

Wt: 12.29 gm. (↘)

Bibliography: Brett, no. 863.

79

Aigai?

AR stater, 520-480 B.C.

Obv. Goat. ΔE ligature.

Rev. Incuse.

Wt: 9.12 gm.

Bibliography: H. Gaebler, *Die Antiken Münzen Nord-Griechenlands,* vol. 3, pt. 2, *Die Antiken Münzen von Makedonia und Pannonia* (Berlin, 1935), 18, no. 3.

80

Asoros?

AR hecte, 520-480 B.C.

Obv. Sphinx.

Rev. Incuse.

Wt: 2.02 gm.

Bibliography: J. N. Svoronos, *L'Hellénisme primitif de la Macédoine* (Athens and Paris, 1919), pl. 17, no. 15-16 attributes larger denominations to Asoros.

81

AR didrachm, 520-480 B.C.

Obv. Rosette. Forepart of boar.

Rev. Incuse.

Wt: 8.55 gm.

Bibliography: Babelon, no. 1851 and 1854.

Locris

82

Opuntian Locrians

AR stater, 369-338 B.C.

Obv. Head of Demeter.

Rev. OΠONTIΩN. Ajax.

Wt: 12.08 gm. (↙)

Bibliography: SNG Berry, no. 570.

Phocis

83

AR hemidrachm, 355-346 B.C.

Obv. Bull's head.

Rev. ΦΩ. Head of Apollo.

Wt: 2.70 gm. (↘)

Bibliography: Brett, no. 972. Mint of Delphi.

Boiotia

84

AR stater, ca. 500 B.C.

Obv. Boiotian shield.

Rev. Θ (in incuse).

Wt: 12.43 gm.

Bibliography: Brett, no. 994. Mint of Thebes.

85

AR stater, 425-395 B.C.

Obv. Boiotian shield.

Rev. ΘΕ. Head of Dionysos.

Wt: 12:26 gm. (↓)

Bibliography: Brett, no. 1006. Mint of Thebes.

86

AR stater, 395-379 B.C.

Obv. Boiotian shield.

Rev. ΘΕ. Head of Dionysos.

Wt: 10.69 gm. (←)

Bibliography: B. V. Head, *A Catalogue of the Greek Coins in the British Museum, Central Greece* (London, 1884), 79, no. 104. Mint of Thebes.

Euboia

87

Eretria

AR drachm, 511-490 B.C.

Obv. E. Cow.

Rev. Octopus.

Wt: 4.01 gm. (↙)

Bibliography: Brett, no. 1028.

88

Karystos

AR didrachm, 313-265 B.C.

Obv. Cow and calf.

Rev. ΚΑΡΥΣΤΙΩΝ. Cock.

Wt: 7.70 gm. (↑)

Bibliography: SNG Berry, no. 610.

89

AR tetradrachm, ca. 525 B.C.

Obv. Gorgoneion.

Rev. Facing head and forepaws of feline.

Wt: 16.68 gm. (↗)

Bibliography: C. T. Seltman, *Athens, its History and Coinage before the Persian Invasion* (Cambridge, 1924), Group K. For the date, C. M. Kraay, "The Archaic Owls of Athens: Classification and Chronology," *NC,* 6th series, 16 (1956), 43-68.

90

AR tetradrachm, 500-480 B.C.

Obv. Head of Athene.

Rev. AΘE. Owl. Olive branch.

Wt: 16.94 gm. (←)

Bibliography: Seltman, *Athens,* Group G i.

91

AR didrachm, 465-450 B.C.

Obv. Head of Athene.

Rev. AΘE. Owl. Olive branch.

Wt: 8.46 gm. (→)

Bibliography: C. G. Starr, *Athenian Coinage 480-449 B.C.* (Oxford, 1970), Group 3.

92

AR drachm, 465-450 B.C.

Obv. Head of Athene.

Rev. AΘE. Owl. Olive branch.

Wt: 4.30 gm. (←)

Bibliography: Starr, *Athenian Coinage,* Group 3.

Aigina

93

AR stater, 479-460 B.C.

Obv. Turtle.

Rev. Incuse.

Wt: 12.24 gm.

Bibliography: Brett, no. 1111; For the date R. R. Holloway, "An Archaic Hoard from Crete and the Early Aeginetan Coinage," *ANSMN,* 17 (1971), 1-21.

94

AR stater, 400-333 B.C.

Obv. Tortoise.

Rev. ΑΙΓΙ and dolphin in incuse.

Wt: 12.02 gm. (→)

Bibliography: SNG Copenhagen (Attica–Aegina), no. 523.

Corinth and Colonies

95

Corinth

AR stater, ca. 470 B.C.

Obv. Koppa. Pegasos.

Rev. Head of Athene. (↗)

Bibliography: O. Ravel, *Les 'Poulains' de Corinthe,* I (London, 1948), no. 234.

96

Corinth

AR stater, 400-338 B.C.

Obv. Koppa. Pegasos. E.

Rev. Head of Athene. Bucranium and tripod.

Wt: 8.58 gm. (↑)

Bibliography: Ravel 2, no. 890.

97

Ambracia

AR stater, ca. 470 B.C.

Obv. A. Pegasos.

Rev. Head of Athene. (↑)

Bibliography: O. Ravel, *The "Colts" of Ambracia, ANSNNM,* 37 (New York, 1928), no. 5.*

Elis

98

AR stater, ca. 475 B.C.

Obv. Eagle clutching hare.

Rev. FA. Thunderbolt.

Wt: 12.23 gm. (↓)

Bibliography: C. T. Seltman, *The Temple Coins of Olympia* (Cambridge, 1921), no. 29.*

99

AR stater, 421-400 B.C.

Obv. Eagle's head. Ivy leaf.

Rev. FA. Thunderbolt in wreath.

Wt: 12.09 gm. (↖)

Bibliography: Seltman, *Temple Coins,* no. 149.*

100

AR stater, ca. 363 B.C.

Obv. Head of Zeus.

Rev. FA. Eagle on column.

Wt: 11.98 gm. (↑)

Bibliography: Seltman, *Temple Coins,* no. 181.*

101

AR stater, 385-365 B.C.

Obv. FA. Head of Hera.

Rev. Eagle in wreath.

Wt: 12.24 gm. (→)

Bibliography: Seltman, *Temple Coins,* no. 293.*

Arcadia

102

Pheneos

AR stater, 362-300 B.C.

Obv. Head of Persephone.

Rev. ΦΕΝΕΩΝ. Hermes and child Arkas.

Wt: 11.71 gm. (←)

Bibliography: Brett, no. 1264-1265.

103

Stymphalos

AR stater, 362-350 B.C.

Obv. Head of Artemis.

Rev. ΣΤΥΜΦΑΛΙΩΝ. Herakles.

Wt: 11.55 gm. (↓)

Bibliography: Brett, no. 1269.

104

Arcadia League

AR hemidrachm, 490-477 B.C.

Obv. Zeus. Eagle.

Rev. A. Head of Artemis. Bow.

Wt: 2.98 gm. (←)

Bibliography: R. T. Williams, *The Confederate Coinage of the Arcadians in the Fifth Century B.C.*, ANSNNM, 155 (New York, 1965), no. 20.* Mint of Cleitor.

105

Arcadian League

AR hemidrachm, 477-468 B.C.

Obv. Zeus. Eagle.

Rev. ΑΡΚΑΔΙΚΟΝ. Head of Artemis.

Wt: 3.03 gm. (←)

Bibliography: Williams, *Confederate Coinage*, no. 57.* Mint of Cleitor.

106

Arcadian League

AR hemidrachm, 477-468 B.C.

Obv. Zeus. Eagle.

Rev. ΑΡΚΑΔΙ. Head of Artemis.

Wt: 3.02 gm. (→)

Bibliography: Williams, *Confederate Coinage,* no. 62.*
Mint of Cleitor.

107

Arcadian League

AR hemidrachm, 468-460 B.C.

Obv. Zeus. Eagle.

Rev. ΑΡΚΑΔΙΚΟ. Head of Artemis.

Wt: 3.02 gm. (↗)

Bibliography: Williams, *Confederate Coinage,* no. 196.*
Mint of Tegea.

108

Arcadian League

AR hemidrachm, 428-418 B.C.

Obv. Zeus. Eagle.

Rev. ΑΡΚΑ. Head of Artemis.

Wt: 2.89 gm. (↑)

Bibliography: Williams, *Confederate Coinage,* no. 311.*
Mint of Mantinea.

109

Arcadian League

AR stater, 370-363 B.C.

Obv. Head of Zeus.

Rev. AR ligature. Pan. Pipes. On rock ΟΛΥΜ.

Wt: 12.29 gm. (↖)

Bibliography: Brett, no. 1260. Mint of Megalopolis.

Aegean Islands

110

Andros

AR stater, 530-500 B.C.

Obv. Amphora.

Rev. Incuse.

Wt: 11.71 gm.

Bibliography: Brett, no. 1285.

Tauric Chersonesos

111

Pantikapaion

AV stater, ca. 350 B.C.

Obv. Head of satyr.

Rev. ΠΑΝ. Lion-griffin holding spear. Ear of wheat.

Wt: 9.11 gm. (↖)

Bibliography: Brett, no. 1350.

Kingdom of Pontus

112

Mithradates VI, Eupator, 120-63 B.C.

AR tetradrachm.

Obv. Head of Mithradates.

Rev. ΒΑΣΙΛΕΩΣ ΜΙΘΡΑΔΤΟΥ ΕΥΠΑΤΟΡΟΣ. Pegasos surrounded by wreath of ivy and berries. Star and crescent. ΧΑΡ ligature.

Wt: 16.61 gm. (↑)

Bibliography: Brett, no. 1355-1357.

Mysia

113
Kyzikos
EL stater, 520-475 B.C.
Obv. Forepart of winged stag. Tunny.
Rev. Incuse.
Wt: 16.0 gm.
Bibliography: Brett, no. 1434.

114
Kyzikos
EL stater, 500-450 B.C.
Obv. Herakles shooting. Tunny.
Rev. Incuse.
Wt: 16.00 gm.
Bibliography: Brett, no. 1462.

115
Kyzikos
EL stater, 450-400 B.C.
Obv. Sphinx. Tunny.
Rev. Incuse.
Wt: 16.4 gm.
Bibliography: Brett, no. 1536.

116
Kyzikos
EL stater, 450-400 B.C.
Obv. Dog biting tunny.
Rev. Incuse.
Wt: 16.25 gm.

117
Kyzikos
EL stater, 400-330 B.C.
Obv. Hermes with amphora. Tunny.
Rev. Incuse.
Wt: 15.76 gm.
Bibliography: Brett, no. 1551.

118
Kyzikos
EL stater, 400-330 B.C.
Obv. Head of Dionysos. Tunny.
Rev. Incuse.
Wt: 16.0 gm.

119
Lampsakos
AV stater, 390-330 B.C.
Obv. Head of Athene.
Rev. Forepart of Pegasos.
Wt: 8.42 gm. (↑)
Bibliography: Brett, no. 1591.

120
Lampsakos
AV stater, 390-330 B.C.
Obv. Head of Zeus. Lotus-tipped scepter.
Rev. Forepart of Pegasos.
Wt: 8.46 gm. (→)
Bibliography: Brett, no. 1594-1595.

121

Lampsakos

AV stater, 390-330 B.C.

Obv. Head of Herakles with woman's stephane. Club.

Rev. Forepart of Pegasos.

Wt: 8.67 gm. (↓)

Bibliography: Brett, no. 1596.

122

Lampsakos

AV stater, 390-330 B.C.

Obv. Head of Aktaion with stag's antler.

Rev. Forepart of Pegasos.

Wt: 8.45 gm. (→)

Bibliography: Brett, no. 1597.

123

Philetairos. 274-263 B.C.

AR tetradrachm.

Obv. Head of Seleukos I Nikator.

Rev. ΦΙΛΕΤΑΙΡΟΥ. Athene. Head of Athene.

Wt: 16.39 gm. (↑)

Bibliography: E. T. Newell, *The Pergamene Mint under Philetairos, ANSNNM, 76* (New York, 1936), no. 10.*

124

Eumenes I, 262-241 B.C.

AR tetradrachm.

Obv. Head of Philetairos.

Rev. ΦΙΛΕΤΑΙΡΟΥ. Athene. Bow. On throne A.

Wt: 16.81 gm. (↑)

Bibliography: U. Westermark, *Das Bildnis des Philetairos von Pergamon* (Stockholm, 1960), obv. XXIX.

125

AR tetradrachm, after 190 B.C.

Obv. Snake emerging from *cista mystica*. Wreath.

Rev. ΠΩΕ ligature and ΑΣ. Two snakes. Bunch of grapes.

Wt: 12.53 gm. (↑)

Bibliography: SNG Berry, no. 973. For the date, E.S.G. Robinson, "Cistophoroi in the Name of King Eumenes," NC, 6th series, 14 (1954), 1-8.

Lesbos

126
Methymne
AR didrachm, ca. 500 B.C.
Obv. MAΘΥΜΝΑΙΟΣ. Boar.
Rev. Head of Athene.
Wt: 8.34 gm. (↙)
Bibliography: Brett, no. 1658-1659.

127
EL hecte, 500-480 B.C.
Obv. Forepart of winged lion.
Rev. Head of cock (incuse).
Wt: 2.57 gm. (↖)
Bibliography: Babelon, no. 2134.

128
EL hecte, 500-480 B.C.
Obv. Forepart of winged boar.
Rev. Lion's head (incuse).
Wt: 2.53 gm. (↑)
Bibliography: Babelon, no. 2141.

129
EL hecte, 500-480 B.C.
Obv. Forepart of winged boar.
Rev. Head of Herakles (incuse).
Wt: 2.53 gm. (↓)
Bibliography: Brett, no. 1673.

130

EL hecte, 500-480 B.C.

Obv. Lion's head.

Rev. Calf's head (incuse).

Wt: 2.58 gm. (↑)

Bibliography: Brett, no. 1680.

131

EL hecte, 500-480 B.C.

Obv. Forepart of bull.Sigma.

Rev. Lion's head (incuse).

Wt: 2.59 gm. (↓)

Bibliography: SNG Berry, no. 1004.

132

EL hecte, 480-430 B.C.

Obv. Forepart of winged lion.

Rev. Sphinx.

Wt: 2.54 gm. (↖)

Bibliography: Brett, no. 1695-1696.

133

EL hecte, 480-430 B.C.

Obv. Male head.

Rev. Helmet. Σ.

Wt: 2.54 gm. (↖)

Bibliography: Brett, no. 1699.

134

EL hecte, 400-350 B.C.

Obv. Female head.

Rev. Lyre.

Wt: 2.53 gm. (↓)

Bibliography: Babelon, no. 2183.

135

EL hecte, 400-350 B.C.

Obv. Head of Artemis. Γ.

Rev. Head of Apollo.

Wt: 2.59 gm. (↑)

Bibliography: Brett, no. 1718.

136

EL hecte, 400-350 B.C.

Obv. Head of Persephone.

Rev. Bull.

Wt: 2.54 gm. (↓)

Bibliography: Brett, no. 1722.

137

EL hecte, 400-350 B.C.

Obv. Head of Apollo.

Rev. Head of Artemis.

Wt: 2.53 gm. (↑)

Bibliography: Brett, no. 1726.

138

EL hecte, 400-350 B.C.

Obv. Head of Athene.

Rev. Head of Hermes.

Wt: 2.59 gm. (↙)

Bibliography: Brett, no. 1733-1734.

139

EL hecte, 400-350 B.C.

Obv. Head of Dionysos.

Rev. Head of satyr.

Wt: 2.53 gm. (↗)

Bibliography: Brett, no. 1736.

140

EL hecte, 400-350 B.C.

Obv. Head of Apollo Karneios.

Rev. Eagle.

Wt: 2.57 gm. (←)

Bibliography: Brett, no. 1738-1739.

141

EL hecte, 400-350 B.C.

Obv. Head of Demeter.

Rev. Tripod.

Wt: 2.56 gm. (↓)

Bibliography: Brett, no. 1742-1743.

Ionia

142

Uncertain mint

EL hecte, ca. 500 B.C.

Obv. Head of Herakles.

Rev. Incuse.

Wt: 2.55 gm.

Bibliography: Brett, no. 1804-1807. The tentative attribution to Samos is doubted by J. P. Barron, *The Silver Coinage of Samos* (London, 1966), 16-17.

Caria

143

Uncertain mint

AR stater, ca. 470 B.C.

Obv. Demon. Ⴞ .

Rev. ꟾⴞ and ⴞMX . Lion.

Wt: 11.51 gm. (↗)

Bibliography: NC, 5th series, 16 (1936), 267 and pl. 14, no. 7 and 8.

Cilicia

144

Mallos–Satrapal Coinage

AR stater, ca. 385 B.C.

Obv. Head of Herakles.

Rev. ΜΑΛ. Head of a satrap.

Wt: 10.11 gm. (←)

Bibliography: Babelon, no. 570.

145

Antiochos IV, 175-164 B.C.

AR tetradrachm.

Obv. Head of Antiochos.

Rev. ΒΑΣΙΛΕΩΣ ΑΝΤΙΟΧΟΥ ΘΕΟΥ ΕΠΙΦΑΝΟΥΣ. Zeus. Victory. ΔΙ ligature.

Wt: 16.53 gm. (↑)

Bibliography: O. Mφrkholm, *Studies in the Coinage of Antiochus IV of Syria* (Copenhagen, 1963), no. 12. Issue of 173-169 B.C.

Bactria–Kingdom

146

Euthydemos I, ca. 230-190 B.C.

AR tetradrachm.

Obv. Head of Euthydemos.

Rev. ΒΑΣΙΛΕΩΣ ΕΥΘΥΔΗΜΟΥ. Herakles. KP ligature.

Wt: 16.50 gm. (↑)

Bibliography: Brett, no. 2236.

147

Antimachos I Theos, ca. 180-170 B.C.

AR tetradrachm.

Obv. Head of Antimachos.

Rev. ΒΑΣΙΛΕΩΣ ΘΕΟΥ ΑΝΤΙΜΑΧΟΥ. Poseidon holding palm and trident. ΔΙΨ ligature.

Wt: 16.68 gm. (↑)

Bibliography: Brett, no. 2239.

Egypt–Kingdom

148

Ptolemy X, 107-88 B.C.

AR tetradrachm.

Obv. Head of Ptolemy I.

Rev. ΒΑΣΙΛΕΩΣ ΠΤΟΛΕΜΑΙΟΥ. Eagle on thunderbolt. LKΘ and ΠΑ.

Wt: 14.23 gm. (↑)

Bibliography: I. N. Svoronos, *Ta Nomismata ton Ptolemaion,* 2 vol. (Athens, 1904), no. 1687. Issue of 88 B.C., Mint of Paphos.

Roman Republic

149

AR denarius, 43-42 B.C.

Obv. L•PLAET•CEST BRVT IMP. Bust of Brutus.

Rev. EID • MAR. Liberty cap between two daggers.

Wt: 3.76 gm. (↑)

Bibliography: BMC II, 480, no. 68.

150

Aureus, A.D. 37-38.

Obv. C·CAESAR·AVG·GERM·P·M TR·POT.
Bust of Caligula.

Rev. AGRIPPINA MAT C CAES AVG GERM.
Bust of Agrippina.

Wt: 7.86 gm. (↖)

Bibliography: BMC I, 147, no. 7.

151

Aureus, A.D. 51-52.

Obv. TI CLAVD CAESAR·AVG·P·M TR P $\overline{XI}$
IMP P P COS $\overline{V}$. Bust of Claudius.

Rev. PACI AVG. Nemesis. Snake.

Wt: 7.67 gm. (↓)

Bibliography: BMC I, 174, no. 68.

152

AE sestertius, A.D. 64-66.

Obv. NERO CLAVDIVS CAESAR AVG GERM P M
TR P IMP P P. Bust of Nero.

Rev. S C DECVRSIO. Nero and squire mounted.

Wt: 32.13 gm. (↓)

Bibliography: BMC I, 227, no. 146.

153

Aureus, A.D. 75-79.

Obv. IMP CAESAR VESPASIANVS AVG. Bust of
Vespasian.

Rev. AETERNITAS. Aeternitas holding sun and moon
before altar.

Wt: 7.29 gm. (↓)

Bibliography: RIC II, 28, no. 121.

154

Aureus, A.D. 81-84.

Obv. DOMITIA AVG IMP DOMITIAN AVG GERM. Bust of Domitia.

Rev. CONCORDIA • AVGVST. Peacock.

Wt. 7.40 gm. (↓)

Bibliography: BMC II, 350, no. 249. For the date, Hunterian I, clxiii.

155

Aureus, A.D. 84.

Obv. IMP CAES DIVI • VESP F DOMITIAN AVG Bust of Domitian.

Rev. GERMANICVS COS $\overline{\text{X}}$. Mourning German woman.

Wt: 7.80 gm. (↓)

Bibliography: BMC II, 307 note.

156

Aureus, A.D. 127.

Obv. AVGVSTVS HADRIANVS. Bust of Hadrian r.

Rev. COS III. Hadrian mounted.

Wt: 7.27 gm. (↙)

Bibliography: BMC III, 293, no. 429 note.

157

Aureus, A.D. 128-137.

Obv. SABINA • AVGVSTA IMP HADRIANI AVG P P. Bust of Sabina.

Rev. CONCORDIA • AVG. Concordia. Cornucopia.

Wt: 7.39 gm. (↓)

Bibliography: BMC III, 353, no. 895.

158

Aureus, A.D. 137.

Obv. L AELIV CAESAR. Bust of Hadrian.

Rev. TRIB POT • COS II CONCORD. Concordia.

Wt: 7.11 gm. (↓)

Bibliography: BMC III, 367, no. 997.

159

Aureus, A.D. 143-144.

Obv. ANTONINVS AVG PIVS P P TR P COS III. Bust of Antoninus.

Rev. IMPERATOR • II. Jupiter.

Wt: 7.08 gm. (↓)

Bibliography: BMC IV, 69, no. 490.

160

Aureus, A.D. 152-153.

Obv. AVRELIVS CAESAR AVG PII FIL. Bust of Marcus.

Rev. TR POT VII COS II. Roma.

Wt: 7.22 gm. (↓)

Bibliography: Hunterian II, 279, no. 16.

161

Aureus, A.D. 163-164.

Obv. • L • VERVS AVG ARMENIACVS. Bust of Verus.

Rev. TR P IIII IMP II COS II REX ARMEN DAT. King Sohaemus of Armenia before Verus and officers.

Wt: 7.27 gm. (↑)

Bibliography: BMC IV, 426, no. 300.

162

Aureus, A.D. 146-161.

Obv. FAVSTINAE AVG PII AVG FIL. Bust of Faustina.

Rev. VENVS. Venus.

Wt: 7.38 gm. (↓)

Bibliography: Hunterian II, 296, no. 7.

163

Aureus, A.D. 147-161.

Obv. DIVA FAVSTINA. Bust of Faustina.

Rev. CONSECRATIO. Peacock.

Wt: 7.23 gm. (↓)

Bibliography: BMC IV, 65, no. 471.

164

Aureus, A.D. 164-169.

Obv. LVCILAE AVG ANTONINI AVG F. Bust of Lucilla.

Rev. VENVS. Venus.

Wt: 7.21 gm. (↗)

Bibliography: Hunterian II, 389, no. 6.

165

Aureus, A.D. 193.

Obv. IMP CAES P HELV PERTIN AVG. Bust of Pertinax.

Rev. PROVID DEOR COS II. Providentia. Star.

Wt: 7.33 gm. (↑)

Bibliography: RIC IV, pt. 1, 8, no. 10.

166

Aureus, A.D. 200-201.

Obv. SEVERVS AVG PART MAX. Bust of Severus with lion's skin.

Rev. IVLIA AVGVSTA. Bust of Julia Domna.

Wt: 7.38 gm. (↓)

Bibliography: RIC IV, pt. 1, 112, no. 161 (b).

167

Aureus, A.D. 217.

Obv. ANTONINVS PIVS AVG GERM. Bust of Caracalla.

Rev. P M TR P XX COS IIII P P. Diana in biga of bulls.

Wt: 6.54 gm. (↗)

Bibliography: RIC IV, pt. 1, 254, no. 284 (c).

168

Aureus, A.D. 270-275.

Obv. IMP C L DOM AVRELIANVS P F AVG. Bust of Aurelian.

Rev. VIRTVS AVG. Mars. Captive.

Wt: 4.82 gm. (↓)

Bibliography: RIC V, pt. 1, 267, no. 15.

169

Aureus, A.D.270-275.

Obv. IMP AVRELIANVS AVG. Bust of Aurelian.

Rev. VICTORIA AVG. Victory. Star.

Wt: 5.08 gm. (↑)

Bibliography: RIC V, pt. 1, 276, no. 96.

170

Aureus, A.D. 283-285.

Obv. IMP CARINVS P F AVG. Bust of Carinus.

Rev. VIRTVS AVGG. Hercules.

Wt: 5.96 gm. (↓)

Bibliography: RIC V, pt. 2, 168, no. 233.

Byzantine Empire

171

Solidus, A.D. 695-698.

Obv. D LEO NPEAV. Bust of Leontius.

Rev. VICTORIA AVGVS CONOB. Cross potent on three steps.

Wt: 4.49 gm. (↓)

Bibliography: C. Morrisson, *Catalogue des Monnaies Byzantines de la Bibliothèque Nationale*, vol. 1 (Paris, 1971), 417.

172

Solidus, Justinian II, second reign, A.D. 705-711.

Obv. DN IhS CGS REX REGNANTIUM Christ.

Rev. DN IUSTINIANUS MULTUS AN   PAX (on globus cruciger). Justinian.

Wt: 4.39 gm. (↓)

Bibliography: Morrisson, *Monnaies Byzantines,* 429.

Professor Watkins was always refining and improving his collections of ancient coins and engraved gems. It is difficult, therefore, to draw conclusions from thirty-four "modern" coins and medals, which may be but a part of what he collected or planned to collect. Quality, as elsewhere, was the dominant, unifying factor. Otherwise, the patterns seem somewhat random, but not entirely so.

The large silver talers of the Holy Roman Empire were favored because they afforded a wide latitude for portraiture and for varied reverse designs, chiefly unusual heraldry. There are a surprising number of talers, dollars, or crowns of Sweden. The Renaissance medals are all relatively late, more a part of Mannerist or early Baroque art than of the relatively austere designs of Pisanello and his imitators. England, more properly the British Isles, is represented by one late Mediaeval gold coin, large and intricate in design, and one Late Renaissance crown of Charles the First. No coins of France are included, but there is a medal relating to the Emperor Napoleon's attempt to cross the English Channel.

If this small segment of a larger collection is to be described in its relationship to Professor Watkins's overall interests, these coins and medals are beautiful, and they are historical. In their visual impact, these numismatic treasures provided the Mannerist, the Baroque, and the Rococo phases of Professor Watkins's collecting. Not overwhelming, but certainly choice.

Cornelius Vermeule and Mary Comstock
Museum of Fine Arts, Boston

Compiler's Note

It is often difficult to tell which side of a Renaissance coin, or medal, is intended to be the obverse and which the reverse. For the sake of uniformity, the side with the portrait has been described first, whether or not such was the intention of the ruler or coiners. All of the coins are silver unless otherwise indicated. Bibliographical citations refer to a specific Watkins coin or medal only where indicated.

Bibliography

J. S. Davenport, *European Crowns 1700-1800* (London, 1964).

J. S. Davenport, *European Crowns and Talers Since 1800* (London, 1964).

J. S. Davenport, *German Talers 1700-1800* (London, 1965).

J. S. Davenport and T. Sondergaard, *Large Size Silver Coins of the World* (Galesburg, Illinois, 1972).

H. A. Seaby, *Standard Catalogue of British Coins* vol. I (London, 1965).

1

England

Richard II, King (1377-1399).

Gold Noble, Type of Edward III.

King standing, facing in ship, with sword and shield.

Rev. Within a tressure of eight arches, floriated cross with a lion in each angle.

Bibliography: H. A. Seaby, *Standard Catalogue of British Coins 1965,* I (London, 1965), 85, no. 1067.

2

United Kingdom, England

Charles I, King (1625-1649).

Crown, 1645, Mint of Exeter.

The King on horseback, a sword in his extended right hand. Tower above, beside name.

Rev. Round shield with coat-of-arms, foliate enrichment around. Tower above, beside date.

Bibliography: H. A. Seaby, *Standard Catalogue of British Coins 1965,* I (London, 1965), 165, no. 2414; J. Schulman, *Catalogue 228* (Amsterdam, February 4-6, 1957), 74, no. 1676.

3

France

Bronze medal, 1613, by Guillaume Dupré (active 1597-1643/7).

Cosimo II, Medici (1590-1620), Grand Duke of Tuscany (1608-1620).

Under the armored bust, at the arm, appears G D F 1613 (G. Dupré fecit). Incuse reverse.

Gaspare or Gasparo Mola appears to have originated this medallic portrait of Cosimo II. He worked in Florence between 1598 and 1627 (C. von Fabriczy, *Medaillen der Italienischen Renaissance* [Leipzig, 1902], 90, fig. 161, with the reverse of Maria Magdalena of Austria).

Bibliography: Leo Hamburger, *Sammlung Vogel, Kunstmedaillen* (Frankfurt am Main, 1924), 12, no. 63, pl. 7; Cf. Bowdoin College Museum of Art, *The Salton Collection* (Brunswick, Maine, 1965), no. 44, silver oval medal by Gaspare Mola (ca. 1580-1640).

4

France

Bronze medal, 1615(?), by Guillaume Dupré (active 1597-1643/7).

Marie de Medici (1573-1642), Queen of France (1600-1631).

Rev. SERVANDO DEA FACTA DEOS.
Marie in a ship manned by men and maidens, two blowing wind-gods above.

Bibliography: Bowdoin College Museum of Art, *The Salton Collection, Renaissance and Baroque Medals and Plaquettes* (Brunswick, Maine, 1965), no. 83 and references.

5

France, First Empire

Bronze medal, 1804-1805, by J. P. Droz.

Napoleon I, Emperor of France (1804-1815).

Struck for the invasion of England, "in London."

Rev. DESCENTE EN ANGLETERRE.
Herakles (presumably France) wrestling a fish-legged man (Triton or a marine Antaios, evidently England).

The group is based on a Graeco-Roman statue of Herakles and Antaios, with strong Neo-Classic modifications.

Napoleon became Emperor from May 18, 1804, and these medals, in silver and bronze, commemorate the events of the year XIII of the French Revolution (September 23, 1804 to September 22, 1805).

Bibliography: See Hôtel Drouot, *Collection J. F.,* Jean Vinchon Sale (Paris, February 22-24, 1971), lot 808, etc.; Münzen und Medaillen A.G., *Auktion 29* (Basel, November 27-28, 1964), 33, under no. 430, Droz's medal for the construction of 2000 invasion barges, and references. The Swiss medallist Jean Pierre Droz was once thought to have had a hand in designing the first United States federal coinage of 1792 to 1793. See C. Vermeule, *Numismatic Art in America, Aesthetics of the United States Coinage* (Cambridge, Mass., 1971), 27.

6

Spain

Alphonzo XII, King (1874-1885).

Five Pesetas, 1876.

Rev. Crowned arms between pillars, the latter entwined by a ribbon bearing the royal motto (PLUS ULTRA).

Bibliography: J. S. Davenport, *European Crowns and Talers Since 1800* (London, 1964), 162, no. 339.

7

Switzerland

Zurich, etc.

Gilded silver "Bundestaler," by Jakob Stampfer, 1555-1556.

Cross in the center of a double circle of shields.

Rev. The "Ruetli Oath," in the year 1296. Three Swiss heroes, the two on the left and right clasping hands.

Albert of Austria sent bailiffs to regulate the free forest lands around Uri and Schwyz. On November 8, 1307 (the year has varied from 1260 to 1334) at the Rütli, Werner von Stauffacher of Schwyz, Walter Fürst of Uri, and Arnold von Melchthal in Unterwalden, each with ten companions (including William Tell), swore to expel the oppressors through a rising on New Year's Day 1308. Versions of this story, and the deeds of the heroes involved (whether fully authentic or not), constitute part of the legendary history of the Swiss Confederation. This coin would commemorate two hundred fifty years of federation, according to the reckoning which places the expulsion of the Austrians in 1296.

Bibliography: L. Mildenberg, *Zürcher Münzen und Medaillen* (Zurich, 1969), 25, no. 131; B. Hobson and R. Obojski, *Illustrated Encyclopedia of World Coins* (New York, 1970), 414.

8

Holy Roman Empire

Habsburg

Maximilian I, Emperor (1508-1519).

Two Talers or Double Gulden, 1509, Struck at Hall im Inntal (Tyrol), dies by Ulrich Ursentaler.

Commemoration of the Coronation at Trent (1508).

Crowned Emperor with imperial trappings.

Rev. Crowned imperial coat-of-arms with subsidiary arms around.

Bibliography: J. S. Davenport and T. Sondergaard, *Large Size Silver Coins of the World* (Galesburg, Illinois, 1972), 89, no. 282A; Münzen und Medaillen A.G., *Auktion 35* (Basel, June 16-17, 1967), 38, no. 303, pl. 20; Münzen und Medaillen A.G., *Auktion 44* (Basel, June 15-17, 1971), 58, no. 715, pl. 40, and comment on the Emperor's own description of the coin.

166

9

Holy Roman Empire

Maximilian of Austria (1459-1519), afterwards Emperor (1508-1519).

Gulden, struck 1511 in memory of his marriage, dated 1479.

Rev. Maria of Burgundy (1457-1482), Maximilian's first wife, in court costume with an elaborate cap.

The portraits are based on those of the noble Neapolitan medallist Giovanni Candida (ca. 1450-1495), who made marriage medals for the royal pair. See Bowdoin College Museum of Art, *The Salton Collection* (Brunswick, Maine, 1965), no. 27. These coins usually show Maria of Burgundy in less formal costume, a low-cut blouse and no elaborate headdress, as the example struck about 1510 in Antwerp (Münzen und Medaillen A.G., *Auktion 23* [Basel, November 7-9, 1961], 61, no. 860, pl. 28).

Bibliography: cf. Münzen und Medaillen A.G., *Auktion 35* (Basel, June 16-17, 1967), 38, no. 304, pl. 20.

10

Holy Roman Empire

Silver medal, 1575, by Antonio Abondio (1538-1596).

Maximilian II, Emperor (1564-1576).

Rev. Maria, his wife (1528-1603), to left, hair in coif, ruff and gown with high collar.

Bibliography: National Gallery of Art, *Renaissance Bronzes from the Kress Collection* (Washington, D.C., 1951), 124, 193 (silver).

11

Austro-Hungarian Empire

(Holy Roman Empire)

Rudolph II, Emperor (1576-1612).

Matthias, King (1608-1612), Emperor (1612-1619).

Taler, ca. 1612, Prague.

Busts of Ferdinand I (1556-1564), Charles V (1519-1556), and Maximilian I (1493-1519), left to right.

Rev. Imperial double eagle with coat-of-arms.

Bibliography: Münzen und Medaillen A.G., *Auktion 44* (Basel, June 15-17, 1971), 63, no. 781, pl. 45. Cf. J. Schulman, *Catalogue 228* (Amsterdam, February 4-6, 1957), 57, nos. 1293, 1294, pl. X; Münzen und Medaillen A.G., *Auktion 23* (Basel, November 7-9, 1961), 62, no. 870, pl. 29 (this reverse for Matthias, Prague, ca. 1612).

12

Austro-Hungarian Empire

(Holy Roman Empire)

Joseph I, Emperor (1705-1711).

Taler, 1707, Struck at Hall (Tyrol).

Rev. Crowned arms, surrounded by the chain of the Golden Fleece.

Bibliography: J. S. Davenport, *European Crowns 1700-1800* (London, 1964), 17, no. 1018.

13

Austro-Hungarian Empire

(Holy Roman Empire)

Charles VI, Emperor (1711-1740).

Taler, 1713, Struck at Hall.

Rev. Crowned double eagle with arms in the center.

Bibliography: J. S. Davenport, *European Crowns 1700-1800* (London, 1964), 27, no. 1050.

14

Holy Roman Empire

Nuremberg

Charles VII of Bavaria, Emperor (1742-1745).

Taler, 1742.

Rev. View of the City, a Radiate Solar (?) Triangle (the
"Eye of God") above. NORIMBERGA.

Charles, Elector of Bavaria, contested Maria Theresa's
right to succeed her father, Charles VI. His most famous
numismatic effort is similar to this coin, a Reichstaler of
1744, dies by J. Thiébaud, showing a view of Augsburg
below the radiate "Eye of God" on one side, AUGUSTA
VINDELICORUM. See Dr. B. Peus, Nachf.,
Münzhandlung, *Katalog 280,* 133, no. 1545, pl. 75.

Bibliography: J. S. Davenport, *German Talers 1700-1800*
(London, 1965), 222, no. 2482. For variations of the
reverse see Dr. Busso Peus, Nachf., Münzhandlung,
Katalog 280 (October 30-November 2, 1972),
144, nos. 1726, 1728.

15

Holy Roman Empire

Francis I, Emperor (1745-1765).

Taler, 1756, Regensburg (Ratisbon).

Rev. A view of the city, the river Danube and its bridges in the foreground.

Bibliography: J. S. Davenport, *German Talers 1700-1800* (London, 1965), 273, no. 2618; Dr. Busso Peus, Nachf., *Katalog 280* (October 30-November 2, 1972), 147, no. 1773, pl. 87.

16

Holy Roman Empire, Low Countries (Flanders)

Joseph II, Emperor (1765-1790), as Count of Flanders.

Crown (Kronentaler), 1782, Brussels mint.

Rev. Floriated cross with three crowns and the Order of the Golden Fleece in the angles. The mintmark, a head, divides the date.

Bibliography: J. S. Davenport, *European Crowns 1700-1800* (London, 1964), 110, no. 1284.

17

Austro-Hungarian Empire

Batthyani

Ludwig, Prince of the (Holy Roman) Empire (1788-1806).

Taler, 1788, Mint of Vienna.

The name I. N. WIRT appears below the draped bust.

Rev. Crowned, mantled, and supported arms.

H. N. Wirt prepared the dies (his name Hans or Hanns being Iohannes in Latin).

Bibliography: J. S. Davenport, *European Crowns 1700-1800* (London, 1964), 72, no. 1184.

18

Austro-Hungarian Empire

Dietrichstein

Ferdinand of Nikolsburg.

Taler, 1695, Mint of Vienna.

Rev. Crowned coat-of-arms, foliate enrichment, and the collar of the Order of the Golden Fleece. Below, monogram of the Mintmaster M. Mittermayer.

Bibliography: Münzen und Medaillen A.G., *Auktion 35* (Basel, June 16-17, 1967), 63, no. 595, pl. 40, and bibliography.

19

Austro-Hungarian Empire

(Holy Roman Empire)

Tyrol, Struck at Hall.

Archduke Maximilian (1602; 1612-1618).

Taler, 1617. Die(s) by Maximilian Gras.

Rev. Crowned coat-of-arms, German cross in the center, volutes on the sides.

Bibliography: Münzen und Medaillen A.G., *Auktion 35* (Basel, June 16-17, 1967), 47, no. 414.

20

Austro-Hungarian Empire

Transylvania

Bethlen Gabor (Gabriel Bethlen, 1613-1629).

Taler, 1621.

Half-figure bust in armor, holding scepter, to right.

Rev. Crowned arms in floriate circle.

Bibliography: cf. Hôtel Drouot, *Collection J. F.,* Jean Vinchon Sale (Paris, February 22-24, 1971), no. 772.

21

Germanic States

Hohenlohe-Ingelfingen

Friedrich Ludwig, Duke (1796-1806).

Taler, 1796, Berlin mint, dies by Abramson.

Rev. X between rosettes.
EINE FEINE MARK.

Duke Friedrich Ludwig was a distinguished Prussian general.

Bibliography: J. S. Davenport, *German Talers 1700-1800* (London, 1965), 170, no. 2356; Dr. Busso Peus, Nachf., Münzhandlung, *Katalog 278* (October 27-29, 1971), 105, no. 2613, pl. 95.

22

Saxony

Friedrich August III, Elector (1763-1827), King (1806-1827).

Taler, 1780, Dresden mint.

Rev. "For the Rewards of Industry."

Below an elaborately-tied wreath appears a landscape with the symbols of commercial and rural prosperity.

This taler is one of a series, with François Boucher-like scenes of children – Amorini engaged in rural pursuits, extolling the virtues of industriousness. Queen Marie Antoinette must have admired these coins.

Bibliography: J. S. Davenport, *German Talers 1700-1800* (London, 1965), 299, no. 2693; Dr. Busso Peus, Nachf., Münzhandlung, *Katalog 278* (October 27-29, 1971), 41, no. 1777, pl. 31, and references.

23

German Republic

Medal by Roth, 1928, commemorating the four hundredth anniversary of Albrecht Dürer's death in 1528.

Dürer's bust facing, after his own self-portrait.

Rev. Saint Paul standing to the left, after Dürer's painting of "Four Apostles" in Munich.

Bibliography: Portrait: M. Mende, *Dürer-Bibliographie* (Wiesbaden, 1971), pl. 8. Painting: V. Scherer, *Dürer* (Stuttgart-Leipzig, 1913), pl. 71; E. Panofsky, *Albrecht Dürer* (Princeton, N.J., 1943), fig. 295.

24

Holy Roman Empire, Italy

Bronze medal, circle of Leone Leoni (ca. 1509-1590) or Jacopo Nizzola da Trezzo (1515-1587 or 1589).

Jacopo de'Medici (1497-1555), Marquess of Marignan (Melegnago), General of Charles V. Bust in armor to right.

Rev. "Whither the Fates may call me."
Pegasos galloping to right, above a forbidding landscape with rocks resembling a monster's jaws.

The medal is certainly posthumous, and it relates to Leone Leoni's monument of Jacopo de'Medici, Marquis of Melegnago, in the Cathedral of Milan, which is said to have been designed by Leoni's mentor Michelangelo (L. Forrer, *Biographical Dictionary of Medallists,* III [London, 1907], 400). Both Leone Leoni and Jacopo da Trezzo used the motto on the reverse of this medal, the former originating it for medals of the imperial family (C. von Fabriczy, *Medaillen der Italienischen Renaissance* [Leipzig, 1902], 99-102). The Emperor Charles V was Leone Leoni's employer when he executed the monument to Charles's general Jacopo de'Medici in Milan.

Benvenuto Cellini made Pegasos a fashionable medallic subject in 1547 when he designed his reverse of a medal for Cardinal Pietro Bembo (1470-1547) (J. Schulman, *Catalogue 236* [Amsterdam, May 1-4, 1962], 96, no. 1921, pl. 33).

25

(Vatican) States of the Church, Rome

Innocent XII (Antonio Pignatelli; 1615-1700), Pope (1691-1700).

Scudo, Year 2 (1693), by Giovanni Hamerani.

Rev. Saint Michael slaying the Dragon. The Pope's coat-of-arms appears in the foreground.

Bibliography: J. Schulman, *Catalogue 239* (Amsterdam, April 5-9, 1965), 167, no. 3546; *Catalogue 236* (May 1-4, 1962), 94, no. 1870, pl. 32.

Holy Roman Empire, Italian Tyrol, Bishopric of Trent (Trident)

Cardinal Bishop Bernardo II di Clesio (1514-1539).

Double Gulden, 1531.

Bust to left, family coats-of-arms amid the inscription. Date in Roman numerals.

Rev. Cardinal Legate's hat above shield with quartered arms. Date in Arabic numerals.

The Counter-Reformation Council of Trent was held in this picturesque city from 1545 to 1563. The Bishopric was secularized and annexed to Austria in 1803.

Bibliography: Adolph Hess, Nachf., *Sammlung Vogel* (Frankfurt am Main, March 25-26, 1929), 71, no. 1199, pl. 31 (this coin). Compare Münzen und Medaillen A.G., *Auktion 23* (Basel, November 7-9, 1961), 64, no. 905, pl. 32; *Auktion 6* (December 6-7, 1946), 25, no. 358, pl. 12, "tallaro largo."

27

Denmark

Christian VII, King (1766-1808).

Speciedaler, 1799, Copenhagen mint.

Bust with unbound hair to right, letters P. G. below.

Rev. Crowned arms in oval shield, with divided date below.

Bibliography: J. S. Davenport, *European Crowns 1700-1800* (London, 1964), 122, no. 1315.

28

Sweden

Gustavus II Adolphus, King (1611-1632).

Taler, 1632, Struck at Augsburg.

Laureate bust in armor, three-quarters to right.

Rev. Crowned shield of Sweden; below, the arms of Augsburg.

The obverse was possibly influenced by the bust of the king made by Georg Petel in Augsburg in the same year (Cahn).

Bibliography: Münzen und Medaillen A.G., *Auktion 29* (Basel, November 27-28, 1964), 59, no. 890, pl. 61; *Auktion 24* (November 16, 1962), no. 291, pl. 22.

29

Sweden

Christina, Queen (1632-1654, died 1689 in Rome).

Riksdaler, 1646, Mint of Stockholm.

Youthful bust of the queen with long hair, three-quarters to the left.

Rev. Christ the Saviour facing, his right hand raised in benediction, his left holding a globe. Crown over three Swedish armorial shields to the left.

Bibliography: cf. Münzen und Medaillen A.G., *Auktion 29* (Basel, November 27-28, 1964), 59, no. 900, pl. 62.

30

Sweden

Charles XI, King (1660-1697).

Taler (Eight Mark), 1693.

Rev. Crowned coat-of-arms, with three crowns on shield. Below the 8–M appear the initials A–S, in script, of the Mintmaster A. Strömner.

Bibliography: cf. Münzen und Medaillen A.G., *Auktion 29* (Basel, November 27-28, 1964), 60, no. 908, pl. 63; *Auktion 44* (June 15-17, 1971), 95, no. 1259, pl. 75.

31

Sweden

Charles XII, King (1697-1718).

Riksdaler, 1709, Struck at Stettin in Pomerania, commemorating the signing of the religious pact of Altranstadt in Breslau.

Rev. Crowned lion with sword in right forepaw, left against a symbolic column, resembling a burning candle.

Bibliography: J. S. Davenport, *European Crowns 1700-1800* (London, 1964), 331, no. 1872.

32

Sweden

Gustavus III, King (1771-1792).

Riksdaler, 1776.

Rev. Crowned arms in a ceremonial (Order) chain.

Bibliography: J. S. Davenport, *European Crowns 1700-1800* (London, 1964), 269, no. 1735.

33

Sweden

Gustavus IV Adolphus, King (1792-1809).

Riksdaler, 1801, by Olof Lidijn.

Rev. Crowned arms in chain.

Bibliography: J. S. Davenport, *European Crowns and Talers Since 1800* (London, 1964), 167, no. 346.

34

Sweden

Charles XIV John (The French Marshal Bernadotte), King (1818-1844).

Riksdaler, 1821, by Borg.

Rev. Portrait medallions of Gustavus Vasa, Gustavus Adolphus, and Frederick I, a palm above and an open wreath below.

Issued for the tercentary of the establishment of political and religious freedom (the Reformation in Scandinavia). The kings on the reverse ruled in 1521, 1621, and 1721.

Bibliography: J. S. Davenport, *European Crowns and Talers Since 1800* (London, 1964), 168, no. 350; B. Hobson and R. Obojski, *Illustrated Encyclopedia of World Coins* (New York, 1970), 411.

1500 copies of the catalogue
designed by Malcolm Grear Designers
type set by Craftsman Type Inc.
have been printed by Meriden Gravure Co.
on Mohawk Superfine
in January 1973